CLIENT-CENTERED
HYPNOTHERAPY

———————————————————■———————————————————

"Look how high I can climb
One step at a time."

CLIENT-CENTERED
HYPNOTHERAPY

R.D. LONGACRE, Ph.D., F.B.H.A

*National Board for Hypnotherapy
and Hypnotic Anaesthesiology*

KENDALL/HUNT PUBLISHING COMPANY
4050 Westmark Drive   Dubuque, Iowa 52002

Contents

Acknowledgments

I wish to thank my many students whom I have had the privilege of teaching on the undergraduate and postgraduate level for their questions that inspired me to do further research and convert my thoughts and experiences into a book.

To Dr. Paul Durbin go my warmest professional regards and sincere thanks for allowing me to present his remarks on "Hypnotherapy and Religion."

I am deeply grateful to Sheila M. Spear, Ct.H.A. for her assistance and research in the area of "Hypnotherapy for Contemporary Women."

I would also like to congratulate my daughter, Leslie Nicole, who in the first nine years of her life taught me the true meaning of "Look How High I Can Climb, One Step At A Time."

Foreword

"Hypnosis just can't be as helpful as you suggest. It is just too easy."

Perhaps you have heard people make statements like this concerning hypnosis. For those who doubt the value of hypnosis, I'd like to tell you this Biblical story found in II Kings 5:1-15 concerning Naamen the leper. Now this story has little to do with hypnosis . . . or does it? It does have something to do with belief and expectation.

If Naaman were to live in our day, he would wear the Medal of Honor and would probably be the Chairman of the Military Joint Chiefs of Staff. He was a proud and successful man who had many servants. Among those servants was a young captive taken in battle with Israel. She was the maid of Naaman's wife. When it was discovered that Naaman had leprosy, she told her mistress of the Prophet Elisha in her home country of Israel. The maid was certain that Elisha could work a miracle and restore Naaman's health.

Following the advice of his wife's maid, Naaman set out for Israel with an official letter from the King of Syria and gold. When he arrived at Elisha's house, Elisha sent a messenger out to greet him. The messenger said to Naaman, "Go and wash in the Jordan seven times and your flesh shall be restored and you shall be cleaned."

Naaman was angry because Elisha did not come out to meet him and perform some spectacular act to restore his health. Instead, a messenger tells him to go wash in the Jordan River. Naaman probably thought to himself, "What a waste of time. We have better rivers in Syria than the Jordan and our rivers cannot heal." Naaman left Elisha's house in anger, but his servant said, "If the prophet had commanded you to do some great thing, would you not have done it? How about following his suggestion that you wash and be healed?"

Dr. Longacre's book teaches you how to build a belief system that works. This belief system is based on expectation and faith in positive outcomes.

When Naaman learned to believe in himself, change became possible. Naamen went to the river Jordan, bathed seven times as instructed and was healed.

Those who have trouble believing that hypnosis can be helpful need to be reminded of the power of one's belief system. Believe it will work, expect it to work, imagine it working, and practice it working. Only as Naaman could believe, expect, imagine, and actually go to the Jordan and wash seven times could he be healed.

We are beginning to understand the unlimited potential of the human mind and its application of hypnotherapy to a myriad of human diseases and other health disorders. In his new book, *Client-Centered Hypnotherapy*, Dr. Longacre, a highly respected national authority on hypnotic anaesthesiology and clinical hypnotherapy, shares his insights and clinical concepts of modern hypnosis which is written in a easy to understand format.

Dr. Longacre includes some very good scripts to use with clients. I admit that I am a believer in the use of scripts when information received from the client is integrated into the script. We can use scripts like a swimmer uses a diving board at a swimming pool. The diving board is the taking off place but the real therapy is getting into the water. This book can be used to help the therapist get into the water. Read it, use it and you will find your ability to help others increases tremendously.

It is an honor to write the Foreword for a trusted friend and respected colleague. I recommend for your reading this valuable contribution of human behavior and self-help therapy to medical, dental, psychological, allied health and holistic professionals.

Paul G. Durbin, Ph.D.
Director, Pastoral Care
Pendleton Memorial Methodist Hospital
5620 Read Boulevard
New Orleans, Louisiana 70127

An Introduction to Client-Centered Hypnotherapy

Hypnosis in its historical context is familiar to most of those involved in the field of hypnotherapy or other professional modalities that incorporate the principles or concepts of hypnosis in their therapeutic work.

These professional health care providers know that the "waxing and waning" of public acceptance and therapeutic viability is becoming a thing of the past. The conceptual understanding of hypnotherapy and clinical application is becoming manifest in many areas of health care.

As the knowledge of hypnosis and its applications continue to multiply, we are literally deluged with new information; so prolific is the publication in this field that it is next to impossible to stay abreast. New and growing knowledge of the brain and its limitless powers has opened an array of therapeutic applications that only a generation ago would have been unthinkable.

During the past ten years, dramatic changes have occurred in the way hypnosis is used in therapy. The client-centered hypno-suggestive approaches that characterize the 1980's are much more resilient, permissive and collaborative than the hypnotist-centered approaches which focus on the ritualistic hypnotic induction procedures and direct suggestions which were still dominant ten years ago.

Our culture is changing. We are more educated. Our information sources are constantly expanding. There is an emerging readiness of large segments of the population to challenge existing authorities. We are living in a time when greater numbers of people are asking for information and tools to expand their understanding and mastery of their own inner worlds.

What does this have to do with us as therapists? The answer is simple: Everything.

For us to rely on traditional hypnotist-centered procedures which focus on ritualistic trance procedures seems increasingly outdated, even quaint.

Although this rigid, dated conception is still prevalent among the public at large, it is not accepted by serious, competent present-day hypnotherapists. Instead, there is a consensus that how a subject responds to hypno-suggestion depends far less than had previously been supposed on the hypnotist's formal induction and far more on the many other complex interrelated variables, most of which pertain to the subject rather than the hypnotist.

These interacting variables which determine responsiveness include: the subject's expectancies and beliefs about hypnosis; the subject's attitudes and motivations toward specific situations; the subject's pre-existing abilities to imagine, fantasize and daydream; the subject's feelings toward and beliefs about the hypnotherapist; and the hypnotherapist's communicative skills in presenting suggestions that are personally meaningful for the particular client or patient.

Therapists using the new hypno-suggestive procedures are aware of the fallacious assumptions underlying the concern with 'trance depth' and they emphasize helping the client or patient learn new skills in utilizing hypno-suggestions for peace of mind, tranquility and self-improvement. There is much more emphasis now on teaching the client or patient a new kind of self-hypnosis.

This new emphasis includes teaching the client or patient with imagery that promotes a calm and focused mental rehearsal of the skills, attitudes and ways of being that the client wants to attain

This approach has indications far beyond the closed therapeutic setting. This type of approach teaches clients and therapists alike to use self-hypnotic rehearsals to attain goals and to function with more focused awareness and proficiency on a daily basis.

The boon and the bane of today's therapist lies in the new insights and skills that are required of competent hypnotherapists. The new observational skills that are emphasized are a boon to the therapist who seeks to break from the dogmas of the traditional teachings of the past.

The challenge of learning new techniques will heighten the awareness and competence of all therapists, whatever their previous level of training or school of thought. The bane of all this new technology, however, is that therapists may become overwhelmed by the explosion of innovation, so much so, that they may be tempted to take the easy route, that of dogmatizing those few approaches they manage to learn and shutting out the rest before he or she thoroughly understands the entire scope of the new field and consolidates it with empirical research.

Although the dynamics of the field of hypnotherapy provide exhilaration at times, we must be careful to acknowledge that it will demand a serious effort on our part to integrate our new knowledge with integrity on both a personal and a professional level.

On a personal level, it will require an open acknowledgement of our need to continually grow in our understanding and skills; on a professional level, it will require the humility to recognize the still limited horizons of our verified knowledge and the need to support/expand the empirical-experimental research required to substantiate and extend what we can only believe we now know.

2

Principle Elements and Concepts of Client-Centered Hypnotherapy

The question most often asked by doctors, dentists, psychologists, hypnotherapists and other health professionals who have attended my lectures and seminars across the nation is, "How do you work with someone who has objections to hypnosis?" Traditionalists believe the correct answer is to educate the client or patient about hypnosis. In other words, dispel the myths of hypnosis and gently persuade the client or patient to accept the modality on the therapist's terms. While this approach is effective in many cases it is contraindicated in client-centered therapy.

A student who has completed a basic course in hypnotherapy will tell you, positive words, statements, affirmations and enhancement of the client's self-esteem are key ingredients to a hypnotherapy session. Negative words like *try, hope, maybe* or thoughts like, *I will* and *I must,* will not allow the client to achieve the results they desire from therapy. When a client has a negative feeling about hypnosis, it does not seem logical to compound that feeling with a reaction that the client is wrong to think that way. It is often said that two wrongs don't make it right. If the way the client thinks is wrong and you tell the client that they are wrong, the client may become even more negative as to expected results from therapy.

As members of the helping professions, we are entitled to our personal and professional opinions regarding hypnotherapy and the techniques we employ. The traditional hypnotist-centered approach with direct suggestions and ritualistic induction procedures has helped millions, but it has also been ineffective for thousands of others. The client-centered therapist is ready to help by giving the individual what they want and the way they want it.

A good illustration of this important concept is the weekday routine of my daughter when she was three years old. It was the custom in our home for me to help Leslie dress in the morning and take her to preschool. My wife left very early to commute to her office. As Leslie and I prepared for the day we discussed what she would be doing in school that day, upcoming family outings and events and why today would be a special day. The concepts presented in our morning routine were not unlike a hypnotherapy session.

While driving Leslie to school, she would invariably ask, "Daddy, will you buy me a treat?" My answer was always positive and then we would discuss what kind of treat she would like to have. Now I realize that I am biased in my opinion of this delightful, intelligent and good natured child, however, I was always amazed at the number of choices she gave to pick from when buying "her" treat.

The list of treats included candy, special good worker or good listener stickers, new clothes for her doll or cookies. Leslie at age three knew what she wanted and how she wanted it (in a bag, the whole bag, a certain color or at a special time).

Rather than argue with her choice of an anticipated reward for learning, growing and developing her potential that day, I would choose one of the items she mentioned and look at it as a category. Candy can be anything that tastes good and is not usually served at dinner time. As a parent I practiced my own form of therapy with my child much the same as I do with clients in my professional work. In teaching Leslie how to grow, I utilized the concept of giving her what she wanted and how she wanted it, but in a way that enhanced her anticipated results from a morning conversation with "Daddy."

Leslie did not know what hypnosis was or what a hypnotherapist was supposed to do. Leslie did know what she wanted to accomplish for herself and the way she wanted me to help her do it. This is the heart of client-centered hypnotherapy. I could have said "no" to candy and tried to explain why candy is bad because it has too much sugar and tried to get her to accept my point of view. I preferred to work within her frame of reference and let her develop her own conclusion about the joy of getting special praise for being the marvelous little person that she was. I am sure that hypnotherapists who employ this concept in their work will be as richly rewarded by comments they receive from their clients as I was when Leslie would walk into my den and announce, "Daddy, your Binky girl is home."

My work as a specialist in hypnotic anaesthesia does not always provide me with the opportunity to explain to each patient or client what hypnosis is or more easily explained, what hypnosis is not. Oftentimes the urgency of the situation leaves no time for any explanation other than, "I am here to help you feel comfortable."

Sometimes I am confronted by a hospital policy that rejects the use of hypnotherapy in their institution. Other times a patient will be overly anxious about my 'powers' as a hypnotherapist or other myths about hypnosis that are equally silly and all too often portrayed by movie characters who know nothing of the art and science of hypnotherapy. As a helping professional, these situations provide me with an excellent opportunity to practice client-centered hypnotherapy.

If a hospital objects to hypnosis, I do not practice hypnosis. In fact, I have never hypnotized anyone in my life. Since all hypnosis is self-hypnosis, all I can possibly do is help teach and guide someone into a self-induced altered state of consciousness. To those who have reservations about hypnosis, I respond with a more acceptable terminology that will facilitate the therapeutic outcome the individual desires. The question is, why is it necessary to compound negatives and then try (a negative) to turn the situation into a positive experience?

The primary purpose of client-centered hypnotherapy is to enable the client or patient to build their own belief system and achieve the goals and outcomes that are important or significant for them at a given time in the present or the future. The terminology preferred by the hypnotherapist is not as important as the end result of the therapeutic work undertaken.

If the circumstance or situation indicates another explanation of the results that can be obtained, the word hypnosis or hypnotherapy can be cast aside and replaced with a term more acceptable to the client. The term "hypnosis" can be replaced with Visualization Therapy, Guided Imagery Therapy, Creative Self-Help Therapy, or Relaxation Therapy. A rose by any other name is still a rose. The therapeutic results of hypnotherapy by any other name are still positive results for the individual who has negative feelings or thoughts regarding the myths or outdated practice of hypnosis.

Brigadier General Paul G. Durbin, Special Assistant to the Chief of Chaplains, Louisiana National Guard, shared a unique approach to client-centered hypnotic induction with me at a convention of clergy hypnotherapists. In addition to his military duties General Durbin is an ordained Methodist minister, chaplain at a large Louisiana general hospital and holds advanced degrees in counseling as well as a doctoral degree in hypnotherapy.

As we talked about my presentation to convention participants on hypnotic anaesthesiology, Dr. Durbin told me about a patient in severe pain who had requested a visit with the chaplain in hope of gaining relief from emotional and physical discomfort. According to Dr. Durbin, this patient was a very religious person and had strong reservations about hypnosis. Dr. Durbin employed a client-centered approach to induction and suggested that they pray together. The following is Dr. Durbin's remarks regarding his session with this patient.

"Prayer hypnosis is a method I use when it would not be suitable to use a traditional induction. I began the prayer; 'As I pray just let yourself relax because the more relaxed you are, the more effective this prayer will be. Now I want you to use your imagination so that the prayer will be even more effective. In Mark 24:11 Jesus seems to be saying that imagery with prayer causes the prayer to be more effective. Jesus said, "Therefore I say unto you, what things soever you desire when ye pray, believe that ye receive them, and ye shall have them."' I used imagery of Jesus placing His hands on the area of discomfort and when the prayer was finished, suggested that the patient could close his eyes when I left and drift into a peaceful and restful sleep." This is an illustration of the clinical application of client-centered hypnotherapy.

In the above case, what the patient wanted was relief from emotional and physical pain, the way he wanted it was in the form of a prayer. Client-centered therapy is not limited to only new and creative techniques, client-centered therapy can also include techniques like a swaying watch or pendulum.

Dr. Cherylanne Dickens, the Director of a nationally recognized hypnotherapy and career training institute in Arizona, shared the following experience with me during a directors meeting of the National Board for Hypnotic Anaesthesiology. "This lady really believed that hypnosis would help her but was concerned about the technique I would use to hypnotize her," said Dr. Dickens. "She explained to me that she could only be hypnotized by a watch and asked me if that was how I did it. My answer was, of course that's how I do it. I asked her to give me a moment to give a message to my receptionist and left the room to find a watch."

The following incident experienced by a Southern California hypnotherapist is a good illustration of another concept of client-centered hypnotherapy.

A young lady had been referred to this therapist by a former client who had explained how the hypnotherapist induced hypnosis by having her put on a set of head phones and listen until she was deeply relaxed. What the referring client failed to explain is that a standard progressive relaxation induction is played through the headset and then the therapist stops the pre-recorded induction and personally gives therapeutic suggestions over a small microphone placed on the corner of his desk.

While the young lady was in the waiting room, she observed another patient putting on a headset in a therapy room and then the door closed. A short time later she was greeted by the therapist who proceeded to place the headset over her ears and asked her to listen while he left the room for a few minutes to get a drink of water. Upon his return, the young lady appeared to be deeply relaxed and in a state of hypnosis. The therapist picked up his headset to hear what the young lady was listening to and how far along she was in listening to the pre-recorded induction tape. To his surprise there was nothing playing, he had forgotten to turn on the tape.

The patient expected to be hypnotized by putting on a headset and listening. She had not been told to listen for a voice or music and believed that by simply putting on a headset she would relax and enter a state of hypnosis. The static and lack of sound in the headset was her client-centered induction.

While the above may be humorous to seasoned hypno-therapists, it illustrates another concept of client-centered hypno-therapy. This concept is; It's not important what you say, what is important is what you don't say.

It is said that a picture is better than a thousand words. Client-centered hypnotherapy is about pictures in the subconscious mind (right brain) and how to make the sights, sounds, colors, feelings and results of these special pictures created by the client have unlimited power.

It was my experience in the 1960s to be greeted by a clerk in a hardware store, clothing store or shoe store who would say, "How can I help you." Now I already knew how he could help me by ringing up my purchase, finding my size or directing me to the appropriate isle where I could find the nails or tools I wanted to purchase. Grammatically his statement was wrong, he should have said, "How may I help you." I didn't mind the grammar because he smiled and seemed to really want to help me.

Though the grammar was incorrect, the concept was sincere and customer-centered. Today it is hard to find a clerk in any store I visit. I wonder if there are any clerks left in our modern society. The term clerk has been replaced with a variety of titles; sales person, consumer counselor, customer service representative or department supervisor.

Many members of the helping professions still cling to the past and forget to smile when they greet you. They are often so preoccupied with proving the validity of a dogmatic approach that they seem to be saying, "How can I help you." Fortunately there is a new awareness and dedication to helping others help themselves by therapists in all the modalities of the helping professions. They are now asking the question, "How may I help you?"

The principle elements and concepts of client-centered therapy can be summarized as: What do you want, How do you want it and how may I help you. The first step in employing these concepts in the practice of client-centered hypnotherapy is to explore how the hypnotic formula of client-centered therapy can be used to facilitate desired therapeutic outcomes for individual clients or groups.

The Hypnotic Formula

Before discussing how to develop client-centered creative induction techniques, the hypnotherapist should be familiar with the concept of the hypnotic formula.

$$(\text{Md. A.})$$
$$H == E + I + B + C$$

The above diagram represents the concept that Self-Hypnosis is the result of Expectation + Imagination + Belief + Conviction and when the client is convinced that they have successfully used the ability of their subconscious mind to accomplish a state of self-hypnosis, the formula becomes even more powerful. You will notice in the diagram that the formula is reversible. In other words, if your work fails to allow the client to logically be convinced that something happened, the formula falls apart and you must start over again. The catalyst of the formula (the factor that makes it work) is Misdirection of Attention (Md.A.). Now let's take a closer look at the various elements of the hypnotic formula.

The prestige of the therapist, establishing rapport and using therapeutic terminology acceptable to the client are important aspects of creating enhanced expectation by the client. I have found in my own practice that the more aware a client is of my clinical experience, advanced training and my professional recognition by other health care providers, the greater their expectation that our time together in a therapy session will be fruitful. My clients generally receive information about my professional background from those referring the client to my office or from articles I have written for various publications. Sometimes they will see a certificate from an advanced training course on my office wall and inquire about the course or conference attended.

I am not suggesting that the hypnotherapist make a special effort to tell the client about their clinical experience or recite selected case histories. However, it would well serve the interests of the client and the therapist to take advantage of opportunities to become visible in the local community. Oftentimes demonstrating hypnotherapy to a community group or civic club, or writing an article for a local publication will enhance the prestige of the therapist and the client's expectation of positive results from therapy.

The following experience will illustrate how prestige and community visibility interact in the clinical setting.

I was attending a convention of hospital and medical employees where I was to speak on the topic of "Alleviating Job Related Stress." Several of the convention participants had attended a lecture I gave several months earlier at a nursing convention and were commenting on an article I had written in a professional journal about "Visualization and Imagery in Nursing." Another participant overheard the conversation and joined the group. After outlining an unpleasant experience with a hypnotist she had hoped would help her with a severe anxiety problem, the group consensus was that she should seek me out at the convention and ask me to refer her to a competent professional in her area.

After introducing herself, this middle-aged woman told me that she was afraid to be hypnotized anymore due to her previous experience, but desperately wanted to overcome her fear of elevators, high places and small rooms. I suggested that we find a quiet alcove in the conference center and talk.

Since she had learned of my professional background and training from a group of medical employees, she had already assumed I would help her and had a heightened sense of expectation. After talking with her I agreed that hypnosis was not the best form of therapy in her case, however, I would teach her a simple technique that she could use to alleviate her discomfort. Without defining the technique or a lengthy explanation of how or why it worked, I asked her to close her eyes and pretend she could see a blackboard with the numbers one to ten written across the top. I then asked her to pretend she was erasing the number ten and when it was gone to nod her head. She proceeded to erase each number the same way and when number one was erased, entered a very nice state of self-hypnosis. This simple induction which took only a few moments was followed by appropriate therapeutic suggestions for her phobias. The technique I taught her was to erase numbers whenever she experienced discomfort on an elevator, in high places or a small room. The technique worked for this woman because she had a heightened sense of expectation that the technique would work.

Before I left the convention the next day, this lady informed me that she could erase the numbers and it significantly helped her when taking the elevator to her room on the 11th floor.

Once a client has enhanced expectation as to therapeutic results, positive thoughts and statements can be formulated to allow him to come to believe that he can accomplish a simple task with mental imagery. This simple task might be something like picturing and imagining biting into a lemon. Many therapists know this imagery as a suggestibility test. The term 'test' is not relevant in client-centered therapy as the term implies you could "fail the test." Client-centered therapy utilizes positive thoughts and outcomes. What is relevant is the role of the catalyst Md.A. in moving the formula forward from expectation to belief.

Utilizing the imagery of holding a lemon, the client is directed to concentrate on the palm of his hand. In other words, misdirect or narrow the focus of all sensory input to a spot on the palm of the hand where an imaginary or 'let's pretend' lemon is supposed to be. By misdirecting attention or narrowing the focus of sensory stimuli, the subconscious mind is able to act on suggestions without interference from the conscious or logical mind.

There are an infinite number of ways to aid a client in misdirecting attention in client-centered therapy. Pretending to erase numbers from a blackboard mentioned earlier is an example of a client-centered technique to misdirect attention. I have demonstrated this concept to students by having them hold a wood chip in the palm of their hand, closing the hand and then imagining all the different shapes the wood chip could be. The way the therapist misdirects attention is limited only by his own creativity in therapeutic work. It is not necessary to abandon older and more conservative techniques to narrow attention, focus or misdirect attention in client-centered therapy. However, the client-centered hypnotherapist should be aware that adherence to hypnotic tradition and dogma is not mandatory if the client, situation or circumstance presents an opportunity to be more flexible in hypno-therapeutic work.

Conviction is the end result of the hypnotic formula and is predicated on carefully helping the client to use the formula to achieve the result they wanted and demonstrating to the client that they have used their own ability to achieve results.

The prestige of the therapist, client expectation and the technique used to help a client enter a state of self-hypnosis are insignificant if the client cannot logically assume that they have entered an altered state of consciousness or utilized their own imagery to effect a positive change in emotional or physical well-being.

The use of convincers and post hypnotic suggestions are ways to demonstrate to a client that they have used their own subconscious ability to enter a state of self-hypnosis to achieve their desired outcome.

Convincers are generally suggested during the therapy session and might be those that produce arm or eye catalepsy. Demonstrating glove anaesthesia, a hand that is stuck to the lap or an arm that floats up into the air are other convincers that may be used. Post hypnotic suggestions might be to find the chair too uncomfortable to sit in unless you stand up and then sit down or finding a writing pen too slippery to hold onto when you return to an awake state. Unfortunately, the use of traditional convincers and post hypnotic suggestions are not appropriate in client-centered therapy.

The use of convincers will facilitate conviction on the part of the client who expected to be hypnotized. But what about the client who has reservations about hypnosis and is expecting positive results with relaxation therapy, visualization therapy, guided imagery or prayer therapy? If careful attention is paid to all aspects of the hypnotic formula, the results will speak for themselves and the patient will reach the stage of conviction without any contrived help by the therapist.

The most effective convincer in client-centered therapy is to suggest a simple exercise that the client can do to induce the same depth of relaxation experienced in the therapy session. This exercise is suggested during the session and after alerting the client have them immediately practice the exercise

The convincer exercise might be to "Close your eyes, take three deep lung cleansing and relaxing breaths and imagine a wonderful, peaceful, tranquil and very safe place and as you do this, you instantly relax as deep as you ever have known yourself to be." Another exercise might be "Close your eyes and pretend to erase all the numbers and as you do, go deeper relaxed and feel all the discomfort fading with each number you erase." The imagery for a convincer exercise can be taken from an imagery script for a specific therapeutic outcome (see guided imagery scripts).

The patient who completes the convincer exercise in your office is now convinced that they can do it on their own and can logically explain to themselves that they have not only learned the technique, but are capable of using it as they choose and when they choose to do so.

Summary

Client-centered hypnotherapy allows the client to participate in the therapy session in a manner that is the most comfortable and acceptable for their desired outcome. If the client is apprehensive about the term hypnosis, another term can be used by the hypno-therapist that is a synonym for an altered state of consciousness.

The elements of the hypnotic formula can be applied to individual clients in a variety of ways so that client expectation and conviction is enhanced.

The most effective types of convincers in client-centered therapy are exercises that allow the client to realize that they have used their own ability and subconscious mind to bring about a positive change in emotional and physical wellness.

3

Client-Centered Induction Techniques

Misdirection of attention is the common component of any induction technique. When working in the area of hypnotic childbirth, hypnodontics and pain management, ritualistic inductions are often time consuming or resisted by the patient due to their intensity of fear, anxiety and tension associated with the medical setting, procedure or understanding of clinical hypnotherapy and hypnosis.

Before the hypnotherapist begins to formulate his own client-centered or creative induction techniques, he should review the concept of misdirection of attention presented in chapter two.

Misdirection of attention can be facilitated by simply changing the subject of the conversation or purposely directing a person's attention to a past experience or something that is not happening now but could possibly happen in the future. Examples might be: "I know you are nervous right now but would you hold my pen for a moment while I explain how it can help you relax." Another example is, "I want you to concentrate on the level of the mercury in this thermometer and as you do, ask yourself this question, will the mercury level stay the same or go higher?" The hypnotherapist may also misdirect attention by saying, "Pick a magic spot on the ceiling and as you concentrate on that magic spot, make it a special place for you to look at, watch, sense and enjoy and you are doing this now and relaxing deeper and deeper and this is so."

In all of these examples the client or patient is narrowing the focus of their conscious mind and becoming more aware of your voice and establishing a subconscious rapport with you and the suggestions that follow. There are over a thousand and one ways to misdirect attention. The question is, how many can you create and employ in your professional work? The answer is an infinite number when you let your own creative subconscious mind experience the possibilities.

It has been said that a picture is better than a thousand words and this is so with hypnotherapy. So why not take the first step in developing your own client-centered or creative induction techniques and picture how a common household item could be used to misdirect attention

Imagine yourself holding a button and pretending to sew it back on your favorite shirt or blouse. Maybe you would prefer to imagine hearing the sound of sewing thread as it weaves back and forth through a beautiful piece of cloth creating a garment of perfect design that is just right for you.

Now take a piece of wrapping paper or stationery, crumple it up and hold it in the palm of your hand. Concentrate on the paper and let your subconscious mind pretend all the things the paper in your hand could be. In your mind's eye let the paper change size, texture, become heavier or lighter or simply change into something else.

If you experience a sense of daydreaming while doing the above exercises, you have successfully misdirected attention and facilitated a light state of hypnosis without relying on a traditional or formal self-hypnosis induction technique.

A double bind type of suggestion is another excellent way to misdirect attention. There are some hypnotherapists who resist this concept, preferring to believe that the double bind suggestion is manipulative and predisposes a situation where the hypnotherapist always wins. I suggest that the double bind technique is the vehicle that allows the client or patient to always win or achieve enhanced belief and conviction that they will "win" their desired outcome with hypnotherapy. The double bind technique actually makes Md.A. (misdirection of attention) a more powerful catalyst to bring the hypnotic formula to fruition in the subconscious mind.

A client-centered creative induction can also be facilitated by using the client's previous hypnotic or daydreaming experiences. These previous experiences of self-hypnosis or waking hypnosis are generally the result of an individual's internal daydreams, imagination or expectations. This type of hypnotic experience may also be due to external suggestions found in advertising slogans, repetitive phrases or innocent suggestions from those the client perceives to be an authority figure.

Listen to yourself singing the following lyrics: *See the USA in a* _____; *M-I-C-K-E-Y* _____; *You'll wonder where the yellow went* _____; or *You deserve a break today so* _____. These are examples of external repetitive suggestions associated with heightened awareness and suggestibility about a desired outcome associated with the music and lyrics used in an advertisement. These musical suggestions may be considered client-centered in that the client has given special meaning or authority to suggestions that are appropriate for a given time, outcome or desired result

The following client-centered induction techniques are the result of a variety of clinical situations and settings and are presented to further illustrate the concept of client-centered induction. The hypnotherapist may use these techniques with selected patients, however, it would better serve the therapist and the client to use these techniques as a guide in developing other techniques for client-centered induction.

Hypnotizing Thermometer

Ask the client or patient to hold the bulb of a bedside thermometer or any other thermometer between the thumb and first finger and watch the level of the mercury in the thermometer. As they do this, give the following suggestions:

Now as you watch the level of the mercury in the thermometer I want you to concentrate on my voice and silently ask yourself the question, will the mercury level go up, stay the same or go down? And as the mercury begins to move what does it mean? If the mercury goes up it means you are enjoying a marvelous sense of warm, restful peace, tranquility and relaxation, and if the mercury goes down you are enjoying a wonderful cool sense of calming relaxation and the mercury can stay the same and you are relaxing very nicely. As you watch the mercury, relaxing deeper and deeper, just close your eyes and listen closely to my voice. Let yourself, allow yourself and now just ignore all the other noises as you relax deeper and in your mind's eye continue watching the level of the mercury in the thermometer. Now let the mercury move in the direction that is so very relaxing for you. Allow it to happen and make it happen now. When the mercury is moving nod your head. (Observe the head movement as this is an ideomotor signal of the client's depth of relaxation).

Now let the mercury move to a number on the thermometer that is appropriate for you. A level and number that is very deeply relaxing and it is so easy to do this and the number is happening and this is so. When the mercury reaches your special, peaceful, relaxing, tranquil and very personal and private number, nod your head please.

If you observe an appropriate ideomotor response, continue with therapeutic suggestions. If you do not observe an appropriate response, continue with the above type of suggestions allowing the client to experience the mercury again moving to the number that has special meaning for them.

Note: It has not been suggested to the client which direction the mercury should move. It has not been suggested that the mercury must move to any given number. The movement of the mercury and the number is client-centered and of no concern to the hypno-therapist. The ideomotor signal of asking the client to nod their head is the client's way of telling the therapist how relaxed they are.

Magic Shape

This induction has been useful for clients who are experiencing acute discomfort associated with trauma or a required medical or dental procedure. The client may be seated in a chair or lying in a bed in a flat or semi-Fowler's position. Begin by asking the client or patient to listen closely to your instructions and follow them without moving their head. Then give the following suggestions:

Now I want you to look straight ahead and pretend to find a magic spot on the wall or ceiling, whichever is directly in front of you. Look for a tiny spot that may have special meaning to you, a spot that magically relaxes you and the spot may have a shape, or a color or just be a tiny point that you know is there and as you watch it relaxing a little bit. And as you watch this spot you are relaxing so very nicely a little at a time. Now without moving your head, lift the pupils of your eyes to another magic spot way above your head. Look up with the pupils of your eyes as high as you can as you relax more and more. Now let your-self, allow yourself to concentrate on this new magic spot way above your head. This new magic spot may have a shape, a color, it may sparkle or shine, change shapes as you watch or just be there as you want it to be.

Now as you watch this magic shape and spot your eyes seem to completely relax and become so very relaxed they want to close. Let that happen now, the eyes close and are so relaxed that your whole body relaxes more and more and the shape of your magic spot seems to fade or not be there and you feel more comfortable as you relax even deeper. The more you relax, the deeper you relax the spot seems to become so very small and tiny and the shape fades away and the more comfortable you are.

Note: The client was allowed to experience or not experience a shape or size and change that experience as they desired without direct suggestions from the therapist. Eye closure was achieved by letting the client feel fatigue in the small eye muscles while watching the spot or shape way above their head.

Slippery Pen

This technique is suited to many occasions where the client or patient has reservations about hypnosis and there is not sufficient time to explain the benefits of hypnotherapy or it is not appropriate to discuss why hypnosis works.

Ask the client or patient to hold your pen between their thumb and first finger and follow your instructions so that by holding the pen they can begin to relax and imagine the therapeutic outcome they desire.

As you gently hold the pen, I want you to gently put the thumb and first finger of your other hand together so that both hands feel like they are holding a pen. As you do this, listen only to my voice, ignore the other sounds around you and watch the hand holding the pen. Watch the hand holding the pen very closely as you relax a little at a time. And the question is, which hand will relax first, the hand with the pen or the other fingers? Now let yourself, allow yourself to feel relaxation in the fingers of the other hand and as you do the hand with the pen relaxes more and more and the pen begins to feel very slippery, like it had a light coating of butter, grease, or oil and as the other hand relaxes between the thumb and first finger the pen begins to slip faster down between the fingers as you relax deeper and deeper sensing, feeling and imagining a relaxing sense of comfort, peace, tranquility and knowing that you are relaxing in a manner that is right for you.

Now watch the pen in your hand and as it begins to become slippery, your other thumb and finger relax even more. And when the other thumb and finger relax, the hand with the pen relaxes so much that the pen just seems to slip from your fingers, and when it does you go even deeper relaxed and are feeling more and more comfortable and relaxed. Now let the pen become slippery and allow yourself to relax deeply so that when the pen drops from your fingers you can close your eyes and go even deeper relaxed, feeling more and more comfortable in any manner that is right for you. Let this happen now, make it happen and enjoy the relaxation and this is so.

Note: The pen was used to misdirect attention. A double bind suggestion; which hand would relax first and trying to concentrate on two hands at the same time was employed. If someone relaxes pressure between one thumb and first finger, they will automatically relax pressure on the other hand much the same as trying to pat the top of their head while moving the other hand in a circular motion over the abdomen. In other words, it takes left brain concentration to make both hands do something different.

Make Believe Friend

This technique helps the client or patient to resolve or remove any objections to entering an altered state of consciousness or self-hypnosis if apprehensive about the circumstances, situation or negative thoughts regarding the desired outcome.

Ask the patient or client to close their eyes and pretend they are visiting with an imaginary friend like they did when they were a youngster or pretend they are visiting with a new imaginary friend they would like to have with them today. Then continue with the following suggestions.

———————————————————■———————————————————

Now you are a special person and have a special friend of your own choosing that can help you relax. Your special friend may be a person in your imagination or a cute, furry and cuddly animal or a special friend you have created to help you in this place and at this time. Now I want you to listen to my voice and pretend that you have a special friend, a make believe friend, and give that friend a name. Your friend can be an animal, a furry little creature, a favorite pet or simply have a size and shape and a color that you pretend it to be. And ask your special friend to tell you how it looks and ask your friend to tell you its name and when you can picture and imagine or just know that your special friend is near you, nod your head please. (Ideomotor signal will indicate that a light state of hypnosis has been achieved).

Very well, as you relax more and more ask your special friend to help you. Ask your special friend if you should give it a special treat or reward for helping you. Ask your special friend to tell you what to do to relax more deeply and as your friend helps you, nod your head please (watch for ideomotor signal).

Now let yourself relax even deeper and bring your special friend along as we enjoy going even deeper and deeper relaxed like we are daydreaming and it is happening and peaceful and calm and relaxing and enjoying all there is to share and learn from your very special, caring and loving friend who is helping you to go even deeper relaxed.

Note: At this point continue with an appropriate deepening technique and therapeutic imagery. This induction allows the client or patient to enter a state of relaxation with a friend of his choosing rather than basing the anticipated outcome on the rapport you have established with him.

Magic Television

This client-centered induction technique is especially suited for children but may also be used with adults. Ask the client or patient to simply close their eyes as if the eyes were very tired from watching a late night TV program and continue with the following suggestions.

I know you enjoy watching TV and think now about the programs you watch. In a moment you can choose a very special TV program that will be relaxing and calming and enable you to become more comfortable than you have ever known yourself to be. I am going to turn on the TV switch now and when I do, the screen will have your favorite program and you are picturing and imagining all the marvelous and wonderful sights, sounds and feelings of your favorite program and I am turning on the switch now. As long as your eyes are closed you are enjoying this wonderful, relaxing, funny, or special program and you can do this as long as your eyes are closed.

Let yourself, allow yourself, to enjoy this marvelous magic TV show and relax even deeper and make it happen now. You are watching the show in your mind's eye or just know how relaxing and comforting it is to go deeper relaxed as you watch the television program in your mind's eye. I can change the channel to another show that relaxes you even deeper. Is that OK with you? Nod your head please (watch for ideomotor response). Very well, I am changing the channel to a show that is deeper relaxing and now you are enjoying this new show and relaxing deeper and deeper and when the picture is in your mind's eye, the let's pretend picture becomes clear and looks so very relaxing and is just the way you want it, nod your head please (watch for ideomotor response).

The hypnotherapist can change channels as needed to deepen the hypnotic state.

Hypnodepthmeter

The concept of the hypnodepthmeter as a way of evaluating the subjective depth of hypnosis and as a deepening technique is presented in *Visualization and Guided Imagery for Pain Management*. This technique can also be used for a client-centered induction.

Ask the client or patient to close their eyes and pretend they can picture or imagine a yardstick leaning against a wall with large easy to read numbers. Then continue with the following suggestions.

This special yardstick has the number 36 at the top and the number one at the bottom and as the numbers become clear and so very easy to see, you are going deeper relaxed and you can see the numbers or just know that they are there. And the numbers have special meaning for you and are yours to use to relax even deeper as I talk with you. And the question is, what do the numbers mean?

And next to the yardstick is an arrow that can point to any number and the arrow becomes clear in your mind's eye as you continue to relax way down and deeper and the arrow can move up and down the yardstick to any number you choose. And this is what the numbers mean. If the arrow is pointing to the numbers 36 deeper down to the number 25 you are experiencing a light state of relaxation. And if the arrow, going even deeper down, points to the numbers 24 to 13 you are in a nice medium state of relaxation and feeling very calm and peaceful and if the arrow going deeper and even deeper down and pointing to the numbers 12 to 1 you are completely and totally relaxed, so very tranquil and calm and more relaxed than you ever thought possible and the arrow is gliding down the yardstick and going to the number that is the special number and the right number for you.

Letting the arrow drift down the yardstick and making it happen now and enjoying relaxing even deeper and when the arrow stops at the special number, the number that is relaxing you deeper and deeper, nod your head please (watch for ideomotor response).

Very well, just let the arrow go even deeper as you ignore all the other sounds around you and concentrate on my voice and you are relaxing even more and deeper and so very much more relaxed now.

Now continue with appropriate therapeutic suggestions.

Blackboard Numbers

This is a client-centered technique that allows the patient or client to write and erase numbers in a matter of moments and enter a nice state of hypnosis.

Ask the client to look at the wall or ceiling and pretend they can picture and imagine a blackboard and each time they take a deep lung cleansing, relaxing breath, they can see the blackboard or just know that the blackboard is there and every time they exhale they are feeling the relaxation as they breathe out all the tension and the blackboard becomes more vivid in their mind's eye. Now continue with the following suggestions.

With each breath, breathing in pure relaxation and exhaling all the tension, pretend you are writing the numbers one to ten on the blackboard and when all the numbers are on the blackboard, close your eyes. If you need a little more time to do this it's OK, just relax with each breath, breathing in pure relaxation and exhaling all the tension as you write the numbers on the blackboard in your mind's eye. And as you close your eyes going deeper relaxed, peaceful, calm and feeling so very good now.

Now closing your eyes I want you to picture and imagine that you are erasing each number beginning with the number ten. When the number ten is gone, nod your head please (watch for ideomotor response). Very well, now let another number disappear, erase the number nine and when it is gone nod your head please. (Continue suggesting that the client erase each successive number and nod their head after each number is gone until the ideomotor signal indicates a light state of hypnosis).

Now erase all the rest of the numbers so that you are in a very nice, deep, relaxing and wonderful state of medical hypnosis and are concentrating only on my voice and going even deeper relaxed. And all the numbers gone, nod your head please.

Note: Misdirection of attention was accomplished when the client began writing numbers on the blackboard. A state of hypnosis was achieved when the numbers were erased and the client indicated this had happened with an appropriate ideomotor response by nodding the head.

Now continue with therapeutic suggestions.

Summary

In the examples given for client-centered, creative induction techniques, the client was given the opportunity to make the suggestions work the way the client wanted them to work.

The importance of numbers or other structured forms of induction imagery was left to the client's imagination rather than dictated by the hypnotherapist.

Misdirection of attention is the principle element of any client-centered induction technique.

Ideomotor signals may be the best determinates of suggestions accepted by the client during a guided imagery induction of hypnosis.

4

Client-Centered Imagery for Selected Therapeautic Outcomes

The essential element of client-centered imagery is positive thoughts and suggestions that enhance the client's desire to achieve their selected outcome. The following scripts emphasize end result imagery that is formulated to be compatible with all three primary learning or accessing systems. These learning or accessing systems are visual, auditory and kinesthetic.

These scripts are intended to illustrate the concept of positive end result imagery, however, they may be used as written in the clinical setting.

Thinking Thin

As you go deeper and deeper now, I want you to picture and imagine yourself on a very beautiful beach, or in a lovely mountain valley or any place you enjoy that is relaxing, peaceful and comforting to you. A special place filled with a thousand happy thoughts and marvelous feelings and where you are so very relaxed and you have lost all the weight. In this special place you are the size and shape you want to be and deserve to be. And you are enjoying all there is to see, to touch, to smell, to hear and this marvelous, happy, peaceful and tranquil place is of your own design and choosing. And you are eating only the amount of food and the kind of food that you know is right for you. And realizing now that you have no desire to trade this wonderful place and feeling for the wrong foods, sweet or fattening food, because you don't need or want them.

Now enjoy sitting down to a beautiful meal and you are eating only the foods and the amount of food that you know is good for you. You are enjoying your meal and chewing your food longer, chewing your food slowly and every single mouthful seems to fill you up so much faster. And you are getting more filling satisfaction out of less food. The less you eat the better you feel, the less you eat the happier you are. The less you eat the more you enjoy your meal and like yourself. And eating only enough to sustain your good health. And that's all you really need and all you really want.

Now I want you to change the scene and pretend that you are trying on some of the clothes in your closet that you couldn't fit into before. You look nice and it feels good to be the size and shape you want to be. And this wonderful feeling is a fantastic reward for thinking thin.

Now pretend you are coming out of the shower and picture and imagine how good you look. You have lost all the unwanted weight. Looking into the mirror and your stomach is nice and flat, thinned out. And you have such wonderful feelings and thoughts about yourself. You are thinking thin and enjoying life more and more each and every day.

Now change the picture again and pretend that you are getting dressed to go out for a very special occasion. And you look and feel wonderful, content, peaceful, and life is so very beautiful and you are a very special and fantastic individual. And you have no desire to trade this new you back for the wrong foods and attitudes about nourishing and healthful food. Before eating anything wrong or even too much of the right food you are thinking and saying to yourself, do I really need this, do I really want this and finding that every time you think thin a wonderful feeling of satisfaction and contentment comes over you.

You are thinking thin and enjoying life more and more every day in each and every way. And changing the things that you want to change, understanding the things that you cannot change and knowing the difference. And you are thinking thin and striving for progress and are now more concerned with progress than you are with perfection.

Non-Smoker

Now as you go deeper and even deeper relaxed, picture and imagine you are in a very beautiful, peaceful and relaxing place, a special place that you always enjoy being. A place of your own design and choosing. And see, touch, feel and listen to all there is in that place that makes it so very wonderful to you. So that if you are at the beach you can feel the gentle warmth of the sun, hearing the sea birds at play and feeling the smooth sand beneath your feet, or if you are in the mountains or walking down a country lane, all the sights and sounds become vivid in your mind's eye and you are more happy and content than you have ever known yourself to be. Go to that place now and enjoy all the wonderful sensations and feelings because you are a non-smoker.

Your heart beats so strong and rhythmically, so effortlessly and pumping life-giving oxygen into the blood and to every tissue and cell in your body. And it's the most wonderful feeling you have ever known all because you are a marvelous person and a non-smoker. Your lungs are nice, clean, pink, healthy tissue now because you are a non-smoker. And enjoying this wonderful feeling of good health you are realizing that you would not trade the treasures of a long and healthy life for a tiny little cigarette.

You wouldn't trade your life or the life of a loved one for a million dollars and certainly not for a tiny little five cent cigarette. And you are a non-smoker and not trying to give up smoking because you are a non-smoker and don't need cigarettes anymore. You don't want them, need them or desire them because you love life so much more and are a non-smoker.

And as you enjoy your special place filled with new health and happiness, you discover that other people smoking around you does not bother you at all. And things that made you think of smoking in the past like talking on the phone, drinking a cup of coffee, finishing a meal or whatever is appropriate for you, now remind you how wonderful it is to be a non-smoker. You are saying no thank you to a cigarette and experiencing a wonderful sense of satisfaction and well being. And a wonderful sense of pride and realizing that you would not trade these feelings for some chopped up weeds wrapped in a piece of burning paper.

You are a non-smoker and your food tastes so much better. Your food is so delicious now that it fills you up faster and for this reason you are not gaining unnecessary weight and you are enjoying all you do so much more. And handling all of your problems with ability and intelligence. And every time you have a thought about a cigarette a pleasant smile comes across your face and a wonderful sense of well-being floods your body, mind and spirit because you are a non-smoker. And every time you have a thought about a cigarette you enjoy more and more your new life filled with a beautiful and satisfying feeling of cleanliness, health, longevity and personal pride. You are trading the forgotten desire for cigarettes for a fantastic treasure chest of rewards that comes to you each and every day and in each and every way as a non-smoker.

Alleviating Unhealthy Stress

And as you continue to drift way down even deeper, relaxing, you are realizing that day by day you are becoming increasingly able to handle all those situations that previously elicited stress, tension and anxiety. And you are doing this so naturally, day by day, in every conceivable way. And you find yourself following certain guidelines. And you no longer resort or fall back to irrational behavior and or habit forming substances.

You are realizing that irritability, shouting, carrying on and fuming do little to alleviate the tension and are often counter-productive. You are confident and a loving person and are realizing that irrational behavior is potentially harmful to yourself as well as friends and family who must bear the brunt of your attacks. And you are releasing all the stress and tension without seeking solace in the consumption of large quantities of alcohol, tobacco or food, since these add physical injury to already strained bodies and minds.

And you have a new and powerful sense of awareness and insight into unhealthy stress. You are recognizing that the danger in a stressful situation is not the actual experience, rather in your individual reaction to it. Stress may be the result of any change in the life situation and the changes can be negative or positive. And since change is a fact of life you are reacting to change that creates stress in a new way. You are now recognizing your own stress signals and taking positive steps to alleviate the stress and definite actions to enrich your life and satisfaction with yourself and others around you.

At the first sign of stress you are withdrawing a bit and taking stock of the situation and your reactions to it. And you are beginning to locate and be aware of the sources that cause stress in your life. And you are making time to take a close and critical look at your personal relationships with people, both important and seemingly unimportant to you. And now finding new ways to make your relationships more meaningful. When appropriate, you are changing the stressful situation by talking to and negotiating with the other person or persons. And if the situation cannot be changed, you are accepting that fact, realizing that there is no written or unwritten law of the universe that says another person must not do whatever it is that stresses you.

It would be nice if people would change and be the way you want them to be, but what is more important is for you to decide what is best for you in any and all situations. The advantages of the job, personal relationships or whatever the life situation might be are not worth the potential disadvantages and effects on your personal health and emotional well-being. And you have a choice in any given situation and you are making the choices that are right for you and you have new abilities and confidence in making the best decisions for you.

You are cleansing your body and mind of unhealthy stress by taking advantage of time to exercise and enjoy recreation or other activities that are pleasurable to you. And you are enjoying thinking positive and happy thoughts as you fall asleep and realize that it is not external events that make you happy or sad, but the attitude you take to these events. And with ever increasing frequency you are learning to accept people and things as they are. And realizing that compromise and reasonable solutions are both necessary and possible and more and more you are substituting the habit of relaxation for the habit of stress.

In stressful situations you are letting the stress go by simply taking a deep breath and as you exhale feeling all the tension and stress leaving the chest area and relaxing and in your mind's eye picturing and imagining how calm, peaceful, intelligent and composed you are. And every time you do this you are relaxing more and more as the stress seems to drift away like a tiny leaf falling from a tree in the fresh breeze of an autumn day. And your marvelous ability to let go of the stress grows stronger every time you say relax and grows stronger each and every day.

Memory and Recall

And going even deeper relaxed you are enjoying a new sense of learning and the art of memory. The art of memory is the art of attention and retention. You must pay attention to anything in order to remember it. For instance when you look at a person and they tell you their name you associate the two if you really want to remember and this is the process that you use to remember anything. And anytime you want to remember you are concentrating your mind, and you look, listen, hear, think, see and associate your mind with the information you wish to retain.

And you have an excellent memory and are improving it every day and paying attention to what is said, what you see and the information you wish to retain so that when you go into your memory bank to make a withdrawal you have already deposited the information you want to withdraw. And the facts are properly stored and ready for you to withdraw anytime you need them. Your memory bank has an unlimited supply of information because you are paying attention and concentrating on the facts, figures, situations or events. And your memory bank is growing each and every day. You no longer work at remembering things, your unlimited memory is a natural process and this is true for every single human being. And you are recalling the deposits made to your memory bank by simply letting your subconscious mind know what you want, anything you want to know then comes into your conscious awareness naturally and easily.

You are relaxing when you make a withdrawal from your memory bank. When the information you are recalling is delayed you are taking a deep breath and forgetting about the process of remembering. And in doing this the information suddenly washes up on the beach of your conscious awareness like a piece of driftwood containing all the information you want. And you are using other skills of memory already stored in your subconscious mind.

Another way to recall is to go through the alphabet to find a particular name. What is the name of that hotel? A, B, C, D, that's it, the Colonial Hotel. The letters are a hook that can go deep down into your subconscious mind and you are using this hook to withdraw answers when you need them. And you are using another tool. Finding something that is misplaced, you are going through the motions or actions associated with the time that you misplaced it and retracing your steps mentally. And when using this tool you are writing a check that is cashed at the memory bank of your subconscious mind.

You are recognizing and realizing how wonderful your memory is and are using the memory system in your subconscious mind. By simply concentrating your attention when making a deposit to your memory bank you are able to recall and withdraw all the information easily and naturally because you are making the proper deposit and discovering new learning and memory tools each and every day.

Better Study Habits

And as you continue to relax now, doing so very well, so peaceful and relaxing even deeper, picture and imagine you are in your favorite place of study, sitting at your desk or table, lying in your bed, at the library or anyplace that is appropriate and comfortable for you.

Now in your mind's eye go to that place and picture and imagine the materials you study with are in front of you and you are ready to begin. And imagine you are placing your hands over your eyes and closing your eyes and relaxing even deeper as outside noises and distractions seem to fade away as you concentrate on the task at hand. And you are shutting out all the noises and distractions and thinking only about the materials you are going to study.

Now concentrate on your breathing, and breathing in pure relaxation and concentration and feeling all the tension leave the chest area as you exhale and your breathing is regular and slow and the distractions fade and you are ready to concentrate on your studies. And all the distractions are gone and your hands slide down from the front of your face and your eyes open and you are totally alert and concentrating only on the material you are studying. And you are concentrating so totally now, concentrating so completely, naturally and effortlessly that you are absorbing the material like a sponge soaking up water. Your subconscious mind is storing all the information so that you are recalling anytime in the future all the material, and you are getting twice as much work done in half the period of time.

The things that used to distract you during your study time no longer bother you. And persons, places, things are no longer distractions and you are very alert and paying attention only to the material before you. And as you concentrate you see and hear only the information that is significant for your studies and nothing else seems important. And you are choosing to ignore anything that interferes with your concentration as you study. And you are noticing that as you concentrate on the material you are able to move your arms, hands, and head because they are free to move along with the rest of your body and you are balanced mentally, emotionally and physically and enjoying the material you are studying.

And you are finding that learning new material is as easy as the technique you now know for improving your ability to remember and recall all the material that you study. And you are pleased to find that by using this technique for improving concentration that you are studying longer and absorbing more and everything that you study is being permanently imprinted in the memory banks of your subconscious mind and you are recalling all of the material by simply taking a deep breath, closing your eyes and allowing the information to naturally, normally and easily flow back into your conscious awareness. And everything you study is going deeply into your subconscious mind and the storehouse of your memories is at your fingertips any time you need it. And every time you use this powerful learning tool it becomes stronger.

Alleviating Examination Anxiety

And as you drift deeper down relaxed, way down relaxing deeper and deeper, let yourself, allow yourself to picture and imagine getting ready for an examination or test and remembering everything you have learned. Just a let's pretend game and in your mind's eye make it happen now and you are recalling all the correct answers easily and naturally with no difficulty because you are properly preparing for and taking examinations in a new relaxed, confident and concentrated manner.

All the information you have deposited in your subconscious mind from your studies is now available to you. When you see or hear the question, your conscious mind is sending down to the subconscious for the answer for you to act upon. The answer is there waiting for you and you are taking the exam with a relaxed body and mind and you are clear and sharp and more confident in your abilities than ever before. When you enter the examination room and pick up the questions you are instantly and easily relaxing and focusing your attention and are so very calm and confident because you know you have studied the information.

And all the nervousness and apprehension seems to disappear and no matter how difficult the question may seem at first sight, you are taking a deep breath and relaxing as the information simply floats up into your conscious awareness. And you are finding that it is easier than you first thought and find it amazing how automatically the answer pops up because you know you have studied and realizing that you will successfully finish the exam with ease and accuracy.

And you are reading all the questions accurately and carefully and you are deciding on the one that you can tackle best and answering that one as fully as you can. And you are not worrying about other questions and completing one question at a time and as you do this you are finding that you actually remember far more than you originally thought you could because all the information you need is available to you.

Now picture and imagine putting down all you know about the first question and choosing the next one that is easiest to answer and you are tackling the next question in the same manner and continuing to answer all the questions until the time is up. And finding now that you have remembered far more than you thought possible when you read or listened to the first question.

Now pretend in your mind's eye that you are turning in your paper and leaving the examination room and you are feeling confident in yourself and rewarding yourself for a job well done. And the test was easy because you are feeling confident and knowing that you had all the information in the memory banks of your subconscious mind and the very question itself triggered your computer and your subconscious mind sent the information back to your conscious mind for you to act upon. And every time you enter an examination room your body and mind completely relaxes and your concentration becomes alert almost like being on an automatic pilot and the computer of your mind warms up as you sit down. And all the information comes easily and naturally every time you begin an exam or test because you have prepared and carefully stored the information you need. And for this reason the information is always there when you want to recall it.

Speed Reading

And as you continue to drift down deeper relaxed, you are recognizing and realizing that the ability to read quickly and accurately and to remember and retain what you are reading is not a skill that a person is born with. It is instead an acquired habit and as such it can be learned.

In fact, those who read the most quickly have learned how to assimilate blocks or chunks of words as they let their eyes scan the written page. And you are learning this skill by listening to suggestions to your subconscious mind that are reasonable, acceptable and in your best interest.

From this day forward, each and every time you are reading you are finding your eyes traveling quickly easily and naturally over the page. There is nothing forced about your reading as it seems easy and relaxed. And you no longer find yourself stumbling over individual words, rather, you assimilate and digest the sentences breaking them down naturally into blocks and chunks.

And your conscious mind aided by your subconscious is automatically picking out those key words or phrases that contain the central idea or theme of the piece you are reading. And discarding the words or phrases that are irrelevant and concentrating only on those that do contain the central idea. And you are reading in this more efficient manner and finding that your subconscious mind automatically catalogues for future reference all that you are reading and the information is automatically available to you whenever you need it, whenever you want it and to assist you with this you are learning a very powerful technique.

Whenever you find yourself in a situation where you have to read quickly and accurately and understand what you are reading, all you have to do is take a deep breath, close your eyes, and as you exhale just picture and imagine you are as calm and relaxed as you are now in this time, in this place and so deeply relaxed. And saying to yourself five times, speed, speed, speed, speed, speed. And you take another deep breath, slowly exhale, open your eyes and begin reading. And as you do this you begin to concentrate, your thoughts narrow down to your reading and all your senses becoming attuned to absorbing your reading. And the rest of the world seems to slowly fade away as your concentration centers on your reading and it remains that way for as long as you are reading that particular piece

Now picture and imagine holding a book of your choice in your hand, feel the book in your hand, open the book and turn to the page of your choice. Now imagine your eyes traveling over the page scanning the written or printed material automatically and naturally. And you are picking out all the pertinent details and reading rapidly with perfect comprehension and remembering and understanding all that you are reading. And you notice that certain phrases just seem to stand out and you can sense both consciously and subconsciously those phrases. And your mind seems to fix and latch onto those particular phrases you are automatically storing and recognizing as important ones.

And you notice how smooth and fluid your reading is and as time passes you are rapidly scanning the pages and reading faster than you have ever done in the past. You are reading more quickly and with much greater understanding, comprehension and remembering what you are reading.

And you are practicing using your new reading techniques and every time you do, your reading becomes even faster because you are a rapid reader.

Freedom From Worry

And continuing to relax and doing so very well now, you are reaching down deeper into your subconscious mind and discovering new insights and thoughts about the wasted effort of worrying and new ways to resolve problems and conflicts in all your daily activities. It is said that 80% of all things we worry about never happen and 15% of the things we worry about are things we can't do anything about. So only 5% of what we worry about is really important. And the small amount of things that are important are being resolved as you are becoming increasingly successful in overcoming worry and finding that there is less and less need to worry about future problems and dangers many of which are quite imaginary.

Now picture and imagine in your mind's eye your abilities to determine the real dangers about the things you fear and finding the possibility of those things actually happening. And understanding that most of the things you worry about never happen and day by day you are finding yourself more and more successful overcoming such pointless and self-defeating worry. You are living one day at a time and making the most of each day and enjoying life more and more in each and every way.

Now see yourself, hear yourself and feel yourself becoming more and more aware of what is happening now in the present and you are responding to what is happening now and not to what has happened in the past or may happen in the future. And you are occupying yourself with only one thing at a time and concentrating all your awareness, responsiveness and energy on the immediate task at hand. You are dealing with each day in a relaxed, peaceful and confident manner free of nervousness and apprehension.

You are realizing that half of all the worry in the world is caused by people trying to make decisions before they have sufficient knowledge on which to base a decision. And you are making your decisions wisely after considering the consequences of your decisions. You are making decisions and resting in the knowledge that you have made a wise decision and then dismissing it from your mind. And you no longer worry about or second guess your decisions and are more flexible in your decisions and making decisions in light of your best present knowledge. And if you require more knowledge you are using your abilities to make a new decision in the light of new knowledge.

And you are finding with each and every passing day that there is little need to think so much about yourself, you are replacing wasted and useless thoughts of worry with pleasant, positive and wholesome thoughts and images. And finding yourself in a situation that formerly elicited worry, you are responding by first choosing all the possible positive outcomes. And you are concentrating on the best possible positive outcome and experiencing it as vividly as possible with all of your senses both physical and emotional. And you are doing this by simply closing your eyes, taking a deep, lung cleansing relaxing breath, and exhaling slowly and picturing and imagining how peaceful and relaxed you are, as peaceful and relaxed as you are now.

You are no longer a slave to self-destructing worry because you have traded the useless habit of worry for a marvelous new and powerful positive mental attitude which has a thousand times more power than any conscious thought to enrich and improve your life.

And you are enjoying all the benefits of positive thinking and you are a confident, assured, intelligent and unique individual with unlimited ability to resolve problems or conflicts without useless worry or negative thoughts.

Self-Confidence

And continuing to relax more and more you are realizing that you are a special person with a strength and the ability that has improved each year and you are acquiring confidence in yourself. And you are allowing a new feeling to develop within you and you are now handling any situation with a new sense of self-confidence. You are a confident person and are using your special and unique abilities to handle any situation you meet and are making decisions wisely. You are making the right decisions after considering the consequences of your decisions and resting in the knowledge that you've made the best decision possible for any situation at any given time. And making a decision to the best of your ability, you are dismissing it from your mind. You are making each decision in the light of your best present knowledge and when acquiring new knowledge making decisions in the light of that new knowledge.

You are a wonderful, unique and marvelous person and you like and respect yourself and because of this others like and respect you. Your circle of friends grows each and every day and you are making new friends because of your own confidence and personality. Each new person you meet is a possible friend and you like people. Because of this people like you and it's easy for you to make new friends and when meeting new people you are realizing your many social assets and confident that people are interested in you.

Now picture and imagine you are meeting people. You are interested in the new people you meet and are totally confident in any social situation. You are confident of your ability to join a group and become part of that group. And you are accepting and enjoying the contribution of others. You are confident in your ability to contribute something to that group and are enjoying yourself at a gathering of new friends and acquaintances. Picture and imagine you are entering a room and you are confident about your appearance and you feel poised and know that you are going to enjoy being a part of the group. See yourself, hear yourself and feel yourself enjoying activities and participating in group activities whatever they might be. You are mixing with the group easily and freely and entering discussions and listening with genuine interest and other people are interested in you. And you are interested in other people's personalities, viewpoints and contributions to the group meeting or party. You have confidence in your ability to join a party, have fun and thoroughly enjoy yourself.

You are feeling good about yourself and are exercising your ability to handle any situation; social, personal or professional and as you continue to go even deeper relaxed you are realizing that if shyness is a particular problem in your life it is the result of an attitude that you have developed which has nothing to do with your true worth as a person. And you no longer need to dwell on negative thoughts or predict failure in any situation. Each and every day you are finding it easy and rewarding to put positive thoughts into your life and becoming increasingly absorbed in some person or thing outside yourself. You are no longer dwelling nearly so much upon yourself and your difficulties or real or imagined shortcomings. And finding yourself feeling more and more independent, you are sticking up for yourself and standing on your own two feet. You are holding your own no matter how difficult or trying things seem to be. You are a confident and caring person, you like others and others like you.

And when you open your eyes in a few moments you are enjoying a new sense of confidence. You are feeling much more contented, happier and more optimistic because you are using your special ability of self-confidence and you are self-assured in any situation or setting. And all of these powerful and positive thoughts are growing each and every day and you are discovering new talents and abilities within yourself as a self-assured and confident marvelous individual.

Insomnia

And relaxing more and more you are letting yourself and allowing yourself to enjoy all the feelings of relaxation and paying attention only to sounds that are relaxing to you as if you were daydreaming or experiencing twilight sleep. And when I alert you in a few moments you are experiencing deep relaxation anytime you desire to do so. And each time you return to this marvelous, peaceful, tranquil and calm state of relaxation you are easily and naturally preparing for a refreshing nap or sleep.

Now I want you to picture and imagine in your mind's eye that you are a lookout, on guard duty or just watching for something to appear in the sky, whatever is appropriate for you. As you concentrate all your senses on this imaginary let's pretend game you are looking forward to a comfortable and refreshing night's sleep. I am going to give you some suggestions that are in your best interest and acceptable, suggestions that are enabling you to. enjoy a wonderful and peaceful period of rest and sleep. Listen to these suggestions that I am giving.

Now you are following these suggestions exactly and in the order I am giving them to you and it is easy to do this as you prepare for sleep. Each night when you go to bed you are relaxing every portion of your body, as relaxed as you are now. And you are doing this without the slightest effort and you are not trying to force yourself to do this. And you are using your subconscious mind to deeply relax because your conscious mind creates a tenseness in your body that defeats its own purpose and you are relaxing unconsciously as you prepare for bed.

And exactly five minutes after your head touches the pillow you are with the greatest of ease relaxing deeper from a daydream and falling into a deep slumber and sleeping so soundly that you have no need to waken before the appropriate time in the morning.

You are awakening in the morning and feeling very refreshed and have the utmost amount of rest as a result of your sleep. You are alert and clear headed when you awaken and looking forward to a marvelous day with positive thoughts and restored energy. And you are carrying on the duties of the day with perfect calmness and a heightened state of alertness and enjoying a wonderful, refreshing and uninterrupted nights sleep.

Now let these suggestions drift all the way down into your subconscious mind and become active and powerful in your life. Let this happen now and make it so. And these beneficial and powerful thoughts are dissolving any of the negative thoughts that interrupt your sleep and you are sleeping soundly because you prepare for bed and expect to go to sleep and sleep without interruption.

When you realize that it is bedtime, you are giving yourself a few moments to think about sleep like if you were on night guard duty or watching the late night sky and then taking a few deep lung filling relaxing breaths and then lying down and watching in your mind's eye the faint twinkling of a star or far off light. Each time you exhale feeling all the tension leaving the chest area and the body and going deeper relaxed into a normal, natural and easy sleep. And you are enjoying a good night's sleep at the end of each and every day.

Procrastination

And as you continue to relax, you are resolving to forgive yourself for the past sins of procrastination. And forgiving yourself for putting off or excusing yourself from the task you know should be completed. Now picture and imagine the new feelings of accomplishment and giving up the punishing guilt of the past in favor of honest regret. And you are leaving the past behind and living in the present.

You are no longer working yourself up into depression over past things left undone. If you haven't done something, you are not by definition a failure. You are merely a person with many positive, negative and neutral thoughts who has just not done something. And you are realizing now that if you can't do or don't want to do something, you are a person who is honest with yourself and with other people involved and you are taking the appropriate action so others can act without you. If you are putting something off because you don't have time or because your time is needed for other things, you are requesting a specific time extension. And you are resolving to be open about your need to delay and accepting your need to finish work or projects you have agreed to complete.

You are setting priorities and recognizing what you have to do, what tasks are more important when your life seems to be disorganized. Picture and imagine you are creating a realistic routine. A routine that will help you keep track of your responsibilities. And you are identifying what you are willing to do with the present to gain something you want in the future. And you are gauging your frustration or tolerance in terms of future rewards, the future rewards that are sufficient to keep you working. You no longer need to procrastinate anymore. You are doing what you really want to do and are setting practical, minimum goals for yourself. And you are breaking down large projects into smaller and even smaller manageable tasks.

You are completing each small task and learning from your success to control your behavior and are able to make instant decisions about issues that have minor consequences. And you are making minor decisions quickly, easily and naturally. Picture and imagine that you are putting on the first appropriate outfit you think of to wear to work, a party or family gathering. Imagine selecting the first appealing item on a luncheon menu without asking others about what you should order.

You are doing small tasks easily from the top of your head and doing small tasks immediately. And if you're busy, small tasks are easy to do. And if you're too busy, you are making a note and doing these tasks as soon as you are free. And you are learning how to trust in your ability to make decisions and focusing on short time intervals.

Now let yourself and allow yourself to feel the sense of accomplishment and sense of well-being completing tasks on time and make that happen now. You are feeling a new pride in yourself and resolving to keep track of your behavior and recognizing what you like to do and what you do not like to do. And you are completing a task you are unsure about and rewarding yourself by doing something you like to do such as reading, working on a hobby, going to a movie or listening to music.

And to help you complete tasks on schedule you are leaving notes for yourself, motivating notes placed where you know you will see them; on a bathroom mirror or refrigerator door or on the center of your car steering wheel. And you are learning to get in touch with your feelings about doing an uncompleted task.

You are trading wasted feelings of anxiety and tenseness and taking risky actions because you are late in beginning a task for a new marvelous sense of accomplishment no matter how small or seemingly unimportant a task might be. And you are rewarding yourself for completing small tasks on time at the time you know it should be done. You are letting go of any performance anxiety and allowing procrastination to fall by the wayside like scattered paper on a breezy day. You are using your marvelous, unique and powerful abilities and are resolute and confident when beginning a task or making a decision. And you are looking forward to the many rewards of completing a task or project in the period of time you know is right for you.

Creativity

And going even deeper relaxed with each and every breath you take and beginning to realize that nobody is born creative. Creativity is something that is inherent in all of us. It is said that by the time the average person has reached the age of 50 they have stored within the memory banks of that marvelous computer we call the human brain, some 70 trillion bits and pieces of information. If a person with a below average IQ has stored 50 trillion bits of information or if a person with an above average IQ has stored 90 trillion they both have more stored information than anyone needs to be creative.

And you are recognizing and realizing that even the most average person has the unlimited potential of acquiring more information. What is important is knowing the difference between those who create and innovate and those who do not. And you are realizing that the creative person is one who knows how to use what information they have accumulated. And you are learning now how to be truly creative.

Nature in her bountiful wisdom has supplied us with not one but two brains. The left brain or left hemisphere of the brain is basically logical and analytical. It draws conclusions based on the logical order of things. We call this process sequential reasoning. The right brain or right hemisphere of the brain uses imagery and is associated with the artistic, musical and creative parts of our being. In most people one hemisphere of the brain is dominant over the other most of the time. The truly creative person, either consciously or subconsciously has learned to bring both sides of the brain into a proper, natural and harmonious balance so that they function together.

Now let yourself relax even deeper and drift back in time and picture and imagine a time when you were particularly creative and inspired. Let yourself travel back to that time now and make it happen. And you are imagining all the surrounding stimuli. Visualize, hear, touch, sense and smell all the objects, people if any and all the things that are there. As you are standing or sitting, notice the temperature, take an inventory of all the things that make this creative moment so very wonderful and special to you.

Now capture all of the emotional creative feelings as you enjoy this moment. Sense all the wonderful feelings of pride and enthusiasm.

Now relaxing even deeper and traveling forward to the future. Traveling to a new time and picturing and imagining completing a project or a project you plan to engage yourself in. And you are enjoying and experiencing this scene with all your senses. Pretend you are completing the work and as you examine it closely you are noticing how very pleased you are with it and yourself. You are a creative person and so very proud because this represents your very finest work.

From this time on you are beginning creative work by taking a few deep relaxing lung cleansing and creative breaths, closing your eyes and relaxing and drifting back to a time when you were filled with creative inspiration. And you are taking a moment and experiencing it as vividly as possible and then saying to yourself create and opening your eyes. And as you do this your brain, like a scale, comes into a creative balance. Take a moment now and picture the two sides of the scale beginning to balance and setting up a harmonious and integrated relationship of enhanced creativity. You may see the scale balancing, feel it balancing or just know that the scale is balanced. And every time you do this you are more and more creative, innovative thoughts and ideas flow like a mountain stream or water from a tap and you are working and creating with joy, determination and drive and you are a talented and creative person.

Each and every day in every conceivable way you are learning something new about yourself and the world around you and this helps you as you become even more creative.

Nail Biting

So easy now to go deeper relaxed and picturing and imagining lovely, beautiful hands and fingers and how nice the neatly trimmed and healthy nails look. And as you go even deeper relaxed recognizing that your nails seem to look and feel so much nicer. And realizing that biting your nails is a habit that you are easily and naturally changing now by trading this non-productive habit for a more satisfying and relaxing one.

You no longer need, want or desire to bite your nails because you never did want to bite your nails. You want, need and deserve healthy looking lovely nails and a deep inner peace and tranquility of relaxation in situations that formerly triggered an unwanted habit.

Now let yourself picture and imagine a wonderful happy and peaceful place. A place that is always filled with wonderful thoughts, relaxation and happy memories. A very special place of your own design and choosing with special meaning to you. And going to this special place now and you are noticing all there is to see, touch, hear, feel and smell that makes this place so unique and relaxing to you. Enjoy all the treasures of your special place.

So that if you are at the beach, the gentle sun warms your body, sea birds dancing and laughing at play and the aroma of the sea breeze mingles with the relaxing rhythm of little waves lapping at the shore. Or if you are in the mountains, the wind whispers through the scented pines and flowers and the warm grassy earth gently supports your body as you look into the bright blue sky with just a few puffy little clouds lazily floating by. And if you are at some other special place you vividly and totally enjoy all there is that is relaxing and comfortable to you. And you are recognizing and realizing that you can return to this special place any time you desire to do so.

And finding that anytime you put your finger to your mouth you are reminded of this special place and by simply closing your eyes you are enjoying this place where you have no desire to bite your nails and your nails are growing more healthy, looking more lovely every time you take a few moments to recall the thoughts of your special place. You are trading an unwanted habit for a marvelous and satisfying feeling of relaxation and enjoying lovely, healthy, manicured and neat appearing nails.

And every time you close your eyes and think to yourself, attractive nails, you are picturing and imagining your nails the way you want them to be and enjoying a new feeling of pride and accomplishment and you have attractive and healthy nails.

Exercise

And as you continue to go even deeper relaxed you are recognizing and realizing that exercise is a normal and natural body process and a part of your everyday living. All of us exercise daily in some way or another without even thinking about it.

Exercise is good for the body, mind and spirit and with exercise comes a wonderful sense of well-being and a radiant glow of good health. Sometimes we do not exercise enough and feel sluggish, tired or lethargic. Sometimes we are overzealous and exercise too much. The important thing you are learning now is that proper exercise always makes you feel good. Proper exercise gives you a sense of well-being and vitality and is an enjoyable experience.

Picture and imagine now that you are preparing to begin a specific exercise that you know is good for your health and your body and mind. And you are beginning your exercise activity by concentrating in your mind on all the benefits and good feelings that exercise will bring. And you are now mentally preparing for whatever exercise routine you choose to enjoy. Now take a few deep lung cleansing and relaxing breaths and pretend you are doing the exercise relaxed and confident and doing that activity easily without unnecessary stress, strain or tension.

And you are seeing yourself and feeling yourself enjoying all the movement and motion of this particular exercise. Your heart and lungs are working together in perfect harmony and fresh clean rejuvenating oxygen is flowing through your entire body. And you are concentrating on your breathing. Feeling how easy, normal and natural it is. All the muscles and organs within the body pulsate with a new sense of health. And you are beginning your exercise routine slowly and making an honest effort to accomplish the goal you have set for yourself for your particular exercise. You are cognizant and aware of the body signals that allow you to pace your exercise so that it is beneficial to your body and mind. And you are completing the exercise activity with a wonderful sense of well-being and renewed health, vigor and vitality.

Every time you prepare to exercise you are looking forward to that particular activity more than ever before. Before you begin your exercise you are simply closing your eyes, taking a few deep breaths and imagining the wonderful feelings and rewards of exercise. Enjoying the marvelous sense of well-being and good health sweeping through your body and you are opening your eyes and beginning the exercise that is appropriate for you.

You are preparing emotionally, physically and mentally for your periods of exercise and enjoying your exercise activities more and more each and every day.

Assertiveness

As you continue to relax even deeper down you are recognizing that you are a unique and valuable person and your ideas and opinions are important to others and you are presenting your thoughts and personal opinion in a concise and relaxed manner. You are a polite and caring person and this enables you to make effective contributions to any discussion or situation. Picture and imagine now that you are an assertive person and pretend in your mind's eye that you are in a discussion or situation and exercising your right to listen to others and be heard by others and participate because you have valuable and worthwhile thoughts and opinions to contribute

Assertiveness is an admirable quality. See, hear and feel yourself as an assertive person. You are saying no when you mean no and always polite and kind and you are able to stand up for your own rights. And you are realizing and recognizing that you are making your thoughts known by telling people what you are thinking in the most appropriate manner. You like other people and other people like you for your qualities of open honesty and concern.

You are an assertive person and letting others know that you have a mind and can speak up for yourself. You are using your assertive abilities to change the things in your life you want to change and understanding the things you cannot change and knowing the difference.

Now let yourself and allow yourself to go even deeper relaxed and make it happen and you are realizing that if you want to change something you are able to tell others exactly how you feel about it in a pleasant and polite assertive manner. Your voice is calm and your manner is kind. You are saying what you really feel, think and what you truly mean and others respect your thoughts and opinions because of this.

Now picture and imagine that you are in a conversation or discussion with someone. And you are making a point and able to say to that person, "No, I think you are wrong." See, feel and hear yourself listening to that person's point of view and you are able to change your mind if that is appropriate for you. And you are participating in the discussion or conversation in an honest, calm, relaxed and natural manner with family, friends or in business situations.

You are a worthwhile, intelligent and caring person and you are assertive in your own unique way. You are letting people know that you have a mind and are thinking relaxed and calm and handling any situation that comes up the way you want to handle it. You are loving your life more and more and finding new rewards and satisfaction in all that you do. You are filled with poise and self-confidence and are assertive in your dealings with others and you are honest and open with others as well as with yourself.

Public Speaking

And as you continue to relax, I am going to present some suggestions that are enabling you to learn effective and powerful techniques of public speaking. Now let yourself and allow yourself to drift even deeper relaxed and concentrate on my voice and the suggestions that are in your best interest and acceptable to you.

And finding now that you really like people and enjoy the company of others. And you enjoy doing things for other people, things that make people happy. Other people sense this loving quality in you and are aware that you like them and return the good feelings of companionship to you. People enjoy your company and like to listen to you and you are at ease when you are with other people.

Picture and imagine you are standing in front of a group of people and you are filled with a marvelous feeling of friendliness for them and you see, hear and sense their friendliness towards you. There is a warmth and sympathy in fellowship radiating from the members of the group to you. This caring group is your audience and they like you and want to hear what you have to show them or say.

Pretend you are standing up in front of the audience now. You are perfectly poised, confident, at ease, relaxed and enjoying sharing with friends. You are interested in the audience and you wish to do things for them. Your sense of friendship is so great that talking to these people is just like talking to a special friend or someone who loves you. And as you speak to the audience you are enjoying the same satisfaction as doing a special favor for a friend or loved one. You are confident and secure and sharing with others who genuinely like you.

As you talk with the audience you are automatically relaxing and your lips are flexible, your mouth is moist, your breathing is natural and easy from the diaphragm.

Your hands are poised and calm and your gestures are flowing spontaneously and freely. Feel your legs strong beneath you and you are more secure and confident because you are with others who genuinely like you Your eyes travel over the audience with a sparkle and there is a smile in your heart and a smile in the way you speak. And the audience is smiling back at you. And you are remembering this picture of you speaking to a group or audience and you are a good public speaker.

And when you speak you are using this proper picture, realizing you are a wonderful public speaker. Before speaking you are using this picture to relax and enjoy participating in the program. You are being introduced and feeling a wave of friendship and understanding flowing from the entire audience. You are alert to smiling faces and others who are concentrating on the valuable information you are sharing. And you are using this mental picture more effectively every time you are about to speak in front of a group.

By simply closing your eyes you are seeing the applause and hearing the friendship of the audience as you begin and finish your speech, presentation or performance. And you are taking a few seconds to do this before each presentation. And every time you do this, you are developing a proper picture and your abilities as a public speaker. Your speaking, stage presence and poise are becoming stronger and more effective every time you stand up in front of a gathering because you are using a proper mental picture.

You are an entertaining, interesting, informative and effective public speaker and all of these suggestions are working for you and growing more effective each and every day in each and every way.

Unhealthy Anger and Hostility

And as you drift way down now, relaxing deeper and deeper you are learning to resolve unhealthy anger and hostility and create a new and healthy way of living. As you continue to relax you are realizing that anger is the most destructive of all our emotions because it lies hidden and unrecognized and causes many types of maladjustment. In guilt we are angry at ourselves. In hate we are angry at the objects of our hatred. In self-pity we are angry at the situations or people who frustrate us. Anger may be overt but often it is insidious with many disguises. Unhealthy anger accounts for many of our miseries. No one can become so emotionally mature that they can completely free themselves of anger, but by minimizing it we can lead happier lives.

When we succeed in shaking off the worn-out clothes of hostility it is often replaced with pity and even amusement at the emotional infants who take hostile thrusts at us. Anger can cause a great amount of distress and many forms of illness. And as you continue to relax even deeper you are realizing that when you are angry your brain is inhibited and you are reduced to something less than your full human potential. You are learning a new way to express yourself and alleviate unnecessary anger and hostility.

You are enjoying a new sense of physical and emotional health and finding that you have a feeling of peace and harmony in situations that used to be disagreeable or uncomfortable. You like people and people like you and you are accepting other people and yourself and you are realizing that each personality is a product of heredity and experience. And you are understanding now that if you had been born with someone else's body and had gone through the exact same experiences and the exact same order of experiences, you would probably act the exact same way they do. And you are growing in wisdom and understanding and accepting others as they are.

A new ability and truth is surfacing from your subconscious mind and you are feeling emotions of sympathy and understanding when others do things that you do not approve of. And you are in complete control of your problems at all times, even what others believe to be stressful and trying conditions. And this gives you a great and wonderful feeling of satisfaction and inner health.

Now pretend in your mind's eye that you are in a situation that used to make you angry. Picture and imagine that you are using your new and powerful abilities and diffusing the angry feelings. You are feeling and expressing only the good healthful emotions of love, sympathy and tolerance of others. You love and respect other people for their good qualities and you forgive them for acts that you disapprove of. And you know that they are doing what anyone else would do with the same body experience and level of awareness.

You are a friendly and loving person and have a kind word and smile for everyone. Your pleasant disposition creates a chain reaction in others and they have pleasant feelings about you and they in turn treat others better because you have made a difference and in understanding others the people you are in contact with treat a growing circle of people better. Your abilities to inspire others is like a rock tossed into a pond and the ripples reach out and sparkle and are signs of your good nature, understanding and tolerance.

You are using your special abilities to smile at those who are angry. And you find it is easy to think clearly and choose the proper words because you are calm, competent and relaxed. You are in complete control of your emotions and only the good and healthy emotions, thoughts and positive reactions are present in your subconscious and conscious mind.

And these healthy emotions are feeding back into your daily living and you are becoming more happy and contented each and every day. You are understanding and forgiving. You are a tolerant person and like yourself and others and are forgiving others for what they have done because you accept others.

These powerful thoughts and techniques of healthy living are growing stronger and more effective in your subconscious mind and you are experiencing personal love for yourself and others every passing day. You are in charge of every situation and expressing yourself with understanding. And you are understanding the things you cannot change and changing the things you can change with a positive feeling of well-being. Your subconscious mind is where the emotions reside and is guiding you into selecting good health emotional responses and you are a friendly, warm, loving and caring person.

Hypnotic Childbirth

Now feel yourself relaxing deeper and deeper with each and every breath. And breathing in pure relaxation and notice all the tension leaving the body as you exhale. And going even deeper relaxed and you are realizing what a marvelous experience the birth of your baby will be. Childbirth is a natural and normal body process and with every normal and natural body process there is no need for unnecessary discomfort, tension or anxiety and all the anxiety or tension real or imagined seems to drift away like a tiny leaf floating down a bubbling mountain stream as you relax deeper and even deeper.

And as you relax even deeper you are picturing and imagining what a wonderful experience it will be, giving birth to the baby growing inside you.

Your baby is now within you, developing, growing and preparing for entry into this world. Let yourself imagine your baby smiling, pretend your baby is looking at you with love and feel your baby snuggling in your arms so content and peaceful, looking into your eyes with love and adoration because you are a wonderful mother.

Your child's birth is a satisfying, rewarding and natural event in your life. Childbirth is a joyful experience and a perfectly natural process of your body. Picture, imagine and feel yourself relaxing during childbirth. You are courageous, confident, and deeply relaxed. All the muscles of the body are working together in perfect harmony during your birth experience. You are alert and aware of all that is happening and you are deeply relaxed. You are not giving birth to your baby now, but realizing how wonderful and marvelous giving birth is in a total and complete state of natural relaxation.

Pretend one group of muscles in your womb is relaxing so that baby can go farther down, other muscles are working to push baby out. All the muscles are working together and you are relaxing even more. See yourself feeling so very good. You are healthy, confident and are using your fantastic ability as a woman to give birth to a beautiful and healthy baby full of peace, joy and relaxation. Imagine the magic sound of your baby's first cry. You are alert, relaxed and peaceful and enjoying all the joy as baby cries and says hello to you.

You are looking forward to the birth of your baby and feeling and sensing the warmth and love of your baby and you are a perfect mother in every way. See your baby's beautiful eyes, feel your baby's soft smooth skin, imagine your baby laughing in your arms, tiny little pink fingers and your baby is so very special and unique in every way.

All of these wonderful and marvelous thoughts and feelings are becoming stronger every passing day as baby continues to develop and grow. You are a caring, loving and extremely competent mother and looking forward to childbirth more relaxed, normal and natural than you have ever known yourself to be.

Dentistry

Drifting down deeper and deeper now and you are picturing and imagining a favorite place you would like to be. A special place of your own design and choosing. A place that is always filled with happy thoughts and memories and so very deeply relaxing to you. And going to that place now and enjoying all there is that makes this place so peaceful and relaxing to you. I am going to alert you in a few moments, but when I do you are returning to the feelings, sights and sounds of peace, tranquility, beauty and deep relaxation you are allowing yourself to experience now. And you are returning to your special place by simply closing your eyes and taking a few deep lung cleansing, filling and completely relaxing breaths.

You are enjoying the deep relaxation of your special place during your entire dental visit just by closing your eyes. As soon as you sit down in the dental chair you feel yourself beginning to relax. The chair is safely supporting your body and your eyes seem to become so very heavy they just want to flutter and close and with each breath your favorite and safe place is becoming more vivid in your mind's eye.

You are aware of other noises and sounds and choosing to ignore any distraction to your deep sense of relaxation and following the directions of those who are helping you and going even deeper relaxed. You are so relaxed now that time just seems to stand still until your dentist tells you your visit is over.

Imagine you are in the dental chair and each time you open your eyes you feel peaceful, calm, and very relaxed and when you close your eyes again, you are going even deeper relaxed. All the sights, sounds and the aroma of the dental office relaxes you totally and completely and you are relaxing even as you enter the office or sit in the waiting room. You are so deeply relaxed during your dental visit that you may even forget how long you were in the office and you are experiencing only feelings, thoughts, sights and sounds of calmness, tranquility and deep relaxation. And every time you visit the dental office you are returning to your safe and comfortable place and enjoying a marvelous sense of deep relaxation and comfort.

Pain Management

And just continuing to drift deeper and deeper down now and so very calm, peaceful and so very very relaxed in body, mind and spirit. And as you drift down deeper relaxed you are realizing how many of us experience sensations that we would regard as unpleasant such as pain, discomfort, tension, stress, strain or anxiety.

And we have already learned one method of dealing with these sensations and that is just breathing deeply and removing all parts of stress. And you are using this technique now and totally and effectively dealing with the unwanted sensations or discomfort you may be experiencing. And you are realizing that the symptoms of unpleasant or unwanted sensations are very subjective experiences. We feel them but, as we know only too well, it is often difficult to consciously modify feelings. It is much easier to modify objects and shapes. And you are learning now to change unpleasant sensations into an object. Letting yourself and allowing yourself to do this now and making it happen. And the object may be something you are seeing, feeling or hearing or something that you just know it to be.

If you have a pain or discomfort or if you feel somewhat tense or anxious just take that unpleasant feeling or sensation and turn it into an object. It can be an abstract shape, without numbered sides or a top or bottom. It can be a concrete shape with easy to see lines. Or it can be a shape with geometric design or a loose irregular circle like a puffy cloud floating, fluttering and changing like a bit of white fluff in a powder blue sky. Whatever shape first comes into your mind's eye is the right shape for you.

And you are recognizing that the first shape is the best shape and any other shape is a conscious judgmental effort and does not have the power of the first shape developed in your subconscious mind. And as you relax even deeper now give that first shape a color and a size and you can give it a size by comparing it to something else or by just knowing the size, and the question is what does the size and the color of your shape mean.

The shape is a symbol of your discomfort and the larger it is the more discomfort you are experiencing and the smaller it is becoming, the more comfort you are experiencing and the more vivid the color the more vivid the discomfort and allowing the color to fade as you relax deeper and even deeper. And you are practicing now making the shape first a little bigger and brighter and then taking a few deep lung cleansing and body relaxing breaths making the shape smaller and the color fades and you are becoming more and more comfortable. And you are realizing that you can make the shape smaller by just imagining it to be smaller or using some easy techniques you are learning now.

If the shape is like a balloon you put a needle into it or kick it away, throw it away or tie it onto the back of a boat, truck, airplane or car and are watching it become smaller as it disappears. And you are letting it become smaller and disappearing like a tiny twig floating down a mountain stream or the leaf of a tree blowing away in a refreshing spring breeze. And you are making this shape smaller and smaller any time you desire to do so by just closing your eyes and taking a few deep lung cleansing and relaxing breaths and picturing and imagining the shape fading every time you exhale all the tension and anxiety.

And concentrating now on any discomfort, tension or anxiety you are feeling and making the shape smaller and it is so easy for you to do this. And wherever and whenever you have unnecessary discomfort you are giving it a shape, giving it a size and then making the shape smaller and the colors fade as the discomfort is leaving your body and you are releasing the tension and anxiety and every time you do this your ability to create a sense of comfort and well-being is enhanced in each and every way.

Financial Success

And as you continue to deeply relax and doing so very well now, you are recognizing and realizing that embodied in your subconscious mind are all the tools and information you are using to achieve financial success. And you are allowing this dynamic information to surface and become a part of your daily living and professional activities.

In order to achieve the rewards in life you truly want, desire and know you can accomplish, you are setting a personal goal. This goal is not what you think you can achieve, rather it is a goal you really want, deserve and desire. You are setting a goal without limits. And it does not matter to you how high your goal is. And you are achieving it if you really want it. Now picture and imagine that you are achieving your goal by walking into a bank and making a withdrawal. And you have all the money, experience, ability and confidence or anything else you need on deposit in this personal success financial bank. Picture and imagine you are filling out a withdrawal slip and itemizing all the things you want to purchase, own or enjoy with this withdrawal.

You may be listing items like a new home, a car you have always wanted, a vacation or trip, new outfit, investments for the future. Whatever the items are, see, feel and hear yourself making a list of those that are important to you. And you are putting the most important item at the top of the list and you are using as many withdrawal slips as you need. Now you are totaling your withdrawal and this is your personal goal available to you. And you are learning that before making your success withdrawal you are checking the balance in your financial success account and making sure that you have deposited enough to cover all the things you want to withdraw.

Hear and feel yourself and imagine that you are answering important questions. What am I willing to do in order to have all that I want. How many hours am I willing to work. What types of jobs or careers do I really want. What am I willing to save from the daily successes in my life. What is really important to me. And you are writing the answers down to keep for your records just like a deposit slip.

Your financial success account is coming into perfect balance and you are making a deposit of all the things, time and genuine desires and effort you choose to deposit and are withdrawing the goal your really want.

You are recognizing that you can have anything you want if you are willing to work hard enough to get it and realizing that work is the key but work doesn't have to be hard, boring or unrewarding. Profitable and rewarding work is leaving you pleasantly tired at the end of the day and you are proud, happy and feeling good about yourself. Work and a job well done makes you feel good about yourself. You are achieving financial success and feeling confident and secure in your ability to reach the goal you know is right for you.

A personal goal is not a dream or make believe. A personal goal is living an ongoing process and your goal is an indicator from your subconscious mind and you are achieving what you really desire, want and deserve. Your abilities in setting goals are having results and you are earning and enjoying the success

You are remembering financial success is as easy as filling out a withdrawal slip or writing a check. In order to make your account balance you are making a list of all the things you really and earnestly want and then setting a goal. You are filling out withdrawal slips by listing all the things you are willing to do in order to make your financial success account balance. You are setting goals each and every day and using the marvelous talents and abilities you already have in the creative memory and learning banks of your subconscious mind. And you are more successful financially and personally with each passing day.

Letting Go Of Guilt

And you are letting yourself and allowing yourself to drift even deeper down and relaxing more and more. And going even deeper relaxed you are realizing that guilt is a form of self-punishment. We punish ourselves for real or imagined wrongs by disturbing vital life function and inviting illness and depression. When we try to rid ourselves of guilt by justifying our thoughts or actions with our conscious mind we often begin to harbor unhealthy feelings and emotions about guilt. The harder we try to justify our guilt the more disruptive and entrenched our guilt becomes in our daily living.

And you are realizing now that harboring guilt serves no worthwhile purpose and doesn't right any wrongs or help anyone or anything. And if you are punishing yourself with feelings of guilt you are actually breaking the laws of nature. Everyone makes mistakes and you have the right to be wrong, but you do not have the right to punish a healthy body and make it sick, even if it belongs to you. You are helping yourself now by learning new ways to handle situations that create unnecessary and unwanted feelings of guilt.

Picture and imagine yourself amending genuine wrongs to the best of your ability and current understanding and awareness. An honest effort is sufficient to get on with living the joyful life you deserve. If you really cause some harm, you are asking yourself what you can do to make things better. You are no longer creating a problem where there is none. And you are resolving now to examine the standards by which you judge yourself. Are they standards you accept or have they been drummed into you by parents, teachers, employers or some other person or situation. And you are asking yourself if these standards are reasonable, necessary and a part of the way you want to live.

You are establishing new and more meaningful standards of emotional peace and tranquility. You are accepting your imperfections and realizing that being perfect may be a noble and spiritual goal, but it is not part of the condition of human life. Perfection is an unattainable goal and ideal and is not a requirement for a worthwhile, joyful and fulfilling life.

You are learning now that people often have to act without full knowledge of the consequences. For example even if they try their best, parents can never know enough to deal perfectly with all the problems of raising a child and all the problems of parenting.

Now picture and imagine that you are using these tools of emotional health and a new sense of awareness in your daily living. You are no longer burdening yourself with unrealistic demands. You are no longer expecting to be free of anger in oppressive situations and there is no need or desire to punish yourself for a lack of purity in thought, word or deed. And each and every day you are recognizing the ways that others may try to make you feel guilty no matter how close they may be to you or how lofty their intentions.

Knowing now that it is impossible to win universal approval no matter how hard you try to mold yourself to external or internal demands. You are realizing that you do not need to please everybody. Since everyone is a unique individual you are allowing them to be responsible for their own feelings and are concentrating on your own life, living well and decently in the present according to the standards that are the most appropriate and comforting to you. You are dealing creatively with other people who criticize and express their own feelings of disappointment.

You are trading unwanted and unhealthy feelings of guilt for new rewards by reviewing what you have actually done that makes you feel guilty and what you are learning from it. And you are facing the fact that you cannot change the past but you are learning from it and using these lessons to create a more rewarding and satisfying present and there is no value to excessive guilt.

Picture and imagine you are throwing the heavy yoke of guilt off your shoulders and forgiving yourself and anyone else because you know that no one is perfect. We are all products of our inheritance and our environment. And with your new knowledge and understanding you are forgiving yourself and starting each day with a clean slate. You are enjoying a marvelous and wonderful sense of freedom, you like yourself and others and are a caring person and because of this people sense your understanding and they like you because of it.

You are radiating love and kindness in all you do and you are forgiving yourself and others for past deeds, real or imagined and are at peace with the world and more important, at peace with yourself. You are turning past and present experiences of guilt into opportunities. Opportunities to find out what your values really are. And you are practicing the art of self-forgiveness and defining what you accept as a good life in the present.

Alleviating Depression

And as you continue to drift deeper and even deeper, so very calm, peaceful and so very, very relaxed, you are recognizing and realizing that depression is a signal to you. Depression is a signal that your life is somehow out of balance and the challenge to you now is finding the source of the signal. The major danger of depression is that it can immobilize you and to overcome this you are now recognizing that depression is an opportunity to learn, to grow and to heal. And it is all right to feel the pain that depression brings and letting that pain alert you to the real problems.

Depression can be the motivating force to revitalize your life and you are asking yourself if depression is a wise and necessary withdrawal from having pushed yourself into to much striving and stimulation. It could be that you have simply worn yourself out in activities and relationships that were not sufficiently nourishing and this is a time to realize what you really value in life. Sometimes depression is caused by a loss of a relationship or a personal defeat that stirs up old unhappy memories about yourself that go far deeper than the immediate situation. If your depression hangs on, you are resolving to explore this possibility and taking advantage of this chance to face that time from the past and build a stronger self for the future.

And if you discover that your depression is caused by some error that you have committed or dissatisfaction with something you have done you are allowing yourself to avoid self-blame. Self-blame is defeating and worse than the error you regret. You are learning that to err is human. You are turning past mistakes into opportunities for future growth and personal accomplishment.

Sometimes you may gain relief and enrich your sense of well-being by expressing your feelings of guilt or anger. And you are remembering to direct the anger at the appropriate target. If you blame the wrong person or circumstance you may feel even more guilty and guilt is often the root of depression. And you are resolving to search for secret resentments that may be the cause of guilt.

And you are learning that depression can be caused by bottled up anger. Anger that we feel about and toward people that we are supposed to love. And you are giving yourself permission to feel anger and express it out loud to yourself. You may even indulge in angry fantasies and finding safe and effective ways to express your anger in your imagination. And you have the ability to do or act to create positive change and you are doing things that are enriching your life and feelings of self-worth and contentment.

You are rewarding yourself for what you do without questioning how well you did it. You are no longer concerned with perfection, rather you find new joy and meaning in positive thoughts and actions. You are taking better care of yourself and giving special attention to your appearance. You are trading the unwanted and hurtful feelings of depression for a satisfying and rewarding feeling of self-esteem and inner peace and contentment. When you are feeling low you treat yourself to something out of the ordinary that you really enjoy. You are rewarding yourself with an activity that restores your sense and feeling of balance and energy. And you are making your own decisions rather than waiting for outside events or other people to passively make them for you.

And you are recognizing things and situations that you cannot change and if you cannot leave the situation or circumstance that is hurtful to you, you are using your new abilities and understanding to prevent reoccurring depression. Day by day you are becoming more successful and making positive and vital steps to become absorbed in all the positive aspects of your life.

Fear of Flying

And just continuing to go even deeper down, way down deeper and deeper and you are recognizing and realizing that you can return to this wonderful place of deep peace and relaxation so very calm and peaceful and relaxed as you are now. And you are enjoying this wonderful feeling of relaxation any time you desire to do so.

It is said that people pay more attention to disasters and accidents reported on television and in newspapers than they do to inspiring or happy stories. For this reason we seem to see and hear more about unpleasant things than we do worthwhile stories and events. And you are realizing now that unpleasant events seldom happen the way it appears in the news. In fact most worries and fears seldom happen to us.

Picture and imagine now that you are going on a magic trip and you are peaceful, calm and looking forward to the most marvelous and relaxing trip of your life. And as each and every second or moment passes you are enjoying this trip more and more. Picture and imagine that you are packing for this trip and getting ready to go to the airport. You are not actually going to the airport, just see, feel and hear all the pleasant and relaxing memories of this new magical and marvelous trip. And you are giving your permission for me to go on this trip with you and be your personal guide.

As we travel to the airport notice how beautiful the sky is. Maybe twinkling little stars or a few puffy little clouds lazily floating by or whatever is appropriate for you. And as we go closer to the airport you are relaxing and looking forward to a marvelous satisfying experience. As we enter the airport you are taking a few deep lung filling and relaxing breaths and relaxing and concentrating on all the happy and positive thoughts and feelings about your trip.

Picturing and imagining now the favorite place you would like to travel to.

This special place is always filled with happy thoughts and memories and is the most wonderful and beautiful place in the world. Your destination is filled with radiant colors, relaxing feelings and delightful sounds and sensations. As we board the airplane you are relaxing even deeper and as you do, your special place begins to become vivid in your mind's eye. And as the plane takes off you are experiencing all the wonderful things that make your special destination so relaxing to you.

And as we travel closer and closer to your destination you are enjoying all the things that make this a magic flight. Noticing how comfortable your seat is, how safely it supports your body. And the flight attendant is smiling and you observe others smiling and relaxing and enjoying a beverage or meal. And you are enjoying the company of a special loved one or friend, a new acquaintance or simply reading or listening to music. And you are as peaceful and relaxed on this special flight as you are now in this time and this place.

It seems as if only a moment in time has passed as the plane lands at your destination. You are feeling marvelous, so relaxed and refreshed from a most enjoyable flight. And you are recognizing and realizing that you no longer need worries or negative feelings about traveling by air. You are trading these unhappy emotions for positive, happy and joyful emotions and thoughts when you fly on any particular occasion that is appropriate for you. And you are experiencing these fantastic and satisfying feelings when you travel by simply closing your eyes, taking a few deep breaths and picturing and imagining your magic destination and very special happy, safe and tranquil place. And you are doing this easily, normally and naturally every time you fly.

I am going to alert you in a moment and when I do you are feeling refreshed and relaxed and as if you have just returned from the most wonderful and enjoyable trip you have ever known and looking forward to all your travels that are appropriate for you.

Fear Of Heights

And going way down and even deeper relaxed you are realizing and learning that you are overcoming your fear of heights by depending on your own sense of control, balance and orientation to the things going on around you. Picture and imagine yourself as a psychological playtime toy. Maybe a Humpty Dumpty who falls and then bounces right back to its feet, or a furry playtime animal that falls from a shelf and then leaps up to an even higher shelf in a bookcase. And you are allowing yourself to play a game that is teaching you how to be in touch with your body. And you are learning now when you are upright and you are bouncing back from any situation or circumstance and landing on your feet.

This is a playtime game you learned long ago and you are realizing now that climbing higher and achieving new heights can be a rewarding experience and lots of fun. See and hear yourself asking some important questions. Questions like, how firmly do I stand? Where do I stand? How do I handle conflicting situations in my life? Where is my center of gravity, center of balance and my center of well-being that keeps me balanced? And you are honestly answering these questions and learning more acceptable and mature ways of dealing with your feelings about heights.

When you first feel uncomfortable in a high place you are pinning down exactly what you are doing, what you are feeling and defining your emotional state or psychological balance at the time.

You are making an inventory of other questions of interest to you. Questions like why do you expect fear to happen only to you? What are you thinking about when you become fearful? Are you fearful of anxieties that occur in many different situations? And knowing the appropriate answers to these questions, you are learning and realizing that there is no cause for your fear of heights and you are maintaining the psychological balance and control you are using now in everyday situations and circumstances that are rewarding and natural for you.

You are exercising valid and natural caution and feeling only the quiet emotions that protect your mind and body and realizing that your fears are surfacing and fading easily because your psychological stance is always protecting and comforting you. And you are practicing improving your psychological sense of well-being and balance. You are confident with heights and feel a sense of well-being in various places. Like working upstairs in an office, looking down from a beautiful scenic view or enjoying the night lights of a sparkling city on a clear evening.

You are feeling more and more comfortable and your fear of heights seems to fade and you are allowing yourself to sample increasingly higher situations and finding that each new situation is far less stressful than you ever imagined it would be.

Fear Of Closed-In Places

And as you continue to enjoy a wonderful sense of relaxation and so very comfortable now, you are learning some new and powerful techniques for expanding small or closed-in places into large comfortable and relaxing areas. And these techniques are simple, easy and you are using them totally completely and effectively anytime you desire to do so.

You are learning now that no outside force is responsible for making you fearful of small places. You are simply responding to the way you are thinking. You are developing a new way of thinking and are in as much control of your emotions as you want to be. You are realizing that you can accelerate your negative emotions leading to feelings of increased fright or panic as easily as you can decelerate your unwanted emotions and discovering feelings of greater calm, tranquility and relaxation than you have ever experienced before. New and positive thoughts and attitudes are growing in your subconscious mind and you are more and more comfortable in small or closed-in places and making them bigger by simply taking a deep breath, closing your eyes and imagining a large comfortable place you would like to be.

Picture you are doing this now and imagine that you are entering an elevator, a special elevator that helps you relax. You are entering the elevator on the tenth floor of the most lovely and beautiful building in the world. Just pretend you are entering the elevator and if you desire you can leave the elevator and choose another one that is even more relaxing and comforting to you. And choosing the elevator that is your way of learning, you are stepping inside. As you turn and face the front of the door you notice that the walls of this elevator are covered with beautiful paneling or textured paper and it seems so large.

Picture and feel the plush carpeting on the floor of the elevator. You wish to go down deeper relaxed on the elevator and you are pushing a button marked "relax" on level one. And you notice now a row of lights across the top of the elevator above the door. Each light has a number and the numbers have special meaning for you. And the question is what do the numbers mean.

The light with the number ten indicates that you are on the tenth floor. Each light with a lower number means you are feeling more comfortable and relaxed and as the numbers become lower and lower you are experiencing deeper feelings of comfort and all the anxiety about small places seems to disappear into open thin air.

The elevator is moving now and as each lighted number comes on and then disappears you are relaxing more and more and your thoughts of closed-in or small places become less and less important as you continue to relax. In a few passing seconds you are at the first floor and the doors open and you are stepping out into a wonderful open place of peace, relaxation and experiencing new feelings and healthy thoughts about small places wherever they might be. You are trading any feelings of discomfort when in closed-in places for feelings of confidence, pride, contentment and self-satisfaction. And you are doing this easily and naturally now and anytime in the future. And you are doing this in a manner that is the most appropriate for you.

You are realizing that fear can be a positive learning tool rather than an enemy. You are practicing developing more self-respect by honestly looking at your fear and working steadily and diligently to expand your thoughts and feelings in closed-in or small places. Knowing now that there is an inner part of you that always protects you and is relaxing you in body, mind and spirit in closed-in places.

And you are trading the fear of closed-in places for the peace, comfort, tranquility and deep sense of well-being that you are using and enjoying more and more each and every day.

Fear Of Water

And as you continue to go even deeper and deeper relaxed you are using this wonderful feeling of relaxation every day in every way as you go near the water. If you put the toes of your feet into water you are relaxing and realizing that water is peaceful and invokes a warm soothing feeling like a relaxing bath and there is no need to expect anything different. You are approaching the water with confidence and you are realizing that the real cause of your anxiety about water is unwanted and useless in your present day situation.

You are recognizing and realizing that water is not the enemy. The enemy is non-productive and negative thoughts that serve no useful purpose and inhibit your enjoyment of swimming, boating, taking a vacation cruise or whatever is appropriate for you. You are realizing now that negative thoughts are useless seconds of worry about situations and events that seldom happen. In fact, these self-defeating thoughts remind you to think about all the positive outcomes and pleasures of enjoying the water. Reminding you of the pleasant sensations of a relaxing bath or shower.

Picture and imagine now that you are watching yourself going down to the water. You are not really going close to the water, only pretending in your mind's eye that you are watching yourself. And you see and feel yourself so very confident, relaxed and looking forward to a happy and enjoyable time and participating in a water activity that is appropriate for you. And as you continue to daydream you see, hear and feel yourself completely enjoying your water activity. All the wasted negative thoughts and feelings about water seem to fade away like the dark of the night giving way to the warming sensation of a summer morning beneath a sparkling brilliant blue and relaxing sky.

You are changing and trading old thoughts and rerun movies as easily as the channel on a TV. And watching now as you are enjoying a rewarding, self-satisfying and wonderful activity on the water, near the water or in the water more than you ever imagined or experienced before.

Now let yourself, allow yourself to look at a new picture, hear new sounds and experience new sensations as you trade outdated and old types of thinking for new and rewarding pleasure and relaxation. And you are experiencing all of the marvelous, wonderful and satisfying feelings, emotions, thoughts and pictures by simply closing your eyes, taking a couple of deep breaths and your thoughts become positive and buoyant in everything associated with water activities.

And each and every day the activities on or near the water are becoming more relaxing and enjoyable as you bask in the warmth of new light and knowledge and confidence about water activities.

Fear Of Crowds

And continuing to go even deeper relaxed, you are learning new ways to handle nervous symptoms you feel when you are in a crowd. You are recognizing and realizing that no outside forces make you tense, anxious or nervous. And in various situations your body is simply responding to the way you are thinking.

You are understanding that panic is a state of physical and emotional shock. Blood vessels may dilate or constrict, you may feel short of breath, sense your heart beating rapidly or even feel light-headed. These feelings are natural warning signals of a potentially dangerous situation. These feelings can also be triggered by imagining a situation that does not really exist. And you are learning now that you are recognizing situations of real potential harm and situations created by feelings of fear, stress, tension and anxiety that you may be creating. And you are taking control of inappropriate feelings and learning how to use this information to enhance your natural sense of well-being.

You are replacing feelings of fear while in a crowd with feelings of peace, comfort and tranquility. You are trading unwanted and wasted thoughts for a new sense of well-being and confidence. Picture and imagine that you are in the middle of a delightful, relaxing and interesting cobblestoned square in a friendly village or small country town. You may be enjoying the relaxing sights and sounds of colorful carts, vendors or displays. Smelling the relaxing aroma of bakery products, flowers or scented candles. And this special place is filled with warm, loving and friendly people. You are in the midst of a crowd and feeling confident and relaxed. Off in the distance you are listening to the soft chimes of a bell tower clock. The clock chimes once, twice, a third time and then a fifth time. It is five o'clock in the afternoon and you have spent a whole relaxing and entertaining day in this special square or village. It has been a delightful and peaceful day. The afternoon sun gently warms your face and a calm and relaxing breeze whispers through the square as you leave to return to your home. You are enjoying the sounds of other happy people and have had a marvelous experience and realizing that an outing or large event can be a wonderful experience. Picture and imagine you are walking on smooth cobblestones worn down over a century of time by shoppers and large numbers of friendly people who come to the square. Notice how comfortable it is to walk over the stones and the peace and contentment you are feeling as you smile to other people and they smile back and say hello to you.

You are realizing that in every crowd you have a friend, you are seeing and feeling the warmth from a smiling face or a laughing child or a courteous gentleman or caring woman. Picture and imagine that person and listen to that person welcoming you to a joyful, happy and relaxing outing be it in the city, in the country, in a park or your very own neighborhood.

Any time you are feeling nervous in a crowd you are taking control and remembering this beautiful and relaxing square. You are simply closing your eyes and imagining all the happy thoughts, feelings and emotions that are there for you to picture, imagine, touch, sense, feel and smell. And every time you do this you are relaxing more and more in gatherings of other people and are so very confident and in control.

Healing Imagery

And as you relax even deeper you are developing a powerful technique for healing parts of your body that have been invaded by disease or injury. You are developing a special friend, personal healer or agent that can travel through the body and heal any part as you relax and concentrate on thoughts of wellness. To help you find this special friend or powerful healer, I want you to picture and imagine a special store or shop with hundreds of shelves of soothing and healing suggestions that can be used by you any time you desire to pick one out and take it home. Picture and imagine browsing through this shop. You may be finding a furry little animal, or a ferocious tiger than can eat up disease causing parasites or organisms. And it might be a special weapon invented in the healing laboratory of your mind or even a magic thought that can change shape, design, and color as you think it to be.

Browse through this special healing store and pick out something that you like and pretend and picture in your mind's eye that you are taking it home with you. Now the question is, how can this healing device, friend, animal or magical machine travel through your body and begin the healing process. And the answer is by giving it a road map and directions to the area to be healed. And you are doing this by simply thinking about a transportation system inside your body. This healing system might be the blood stream, or the breathing system or secret tunnels and passages that you know. You are telling your healing agent the best path to follow and giving it permission to heal the invaded or injured area, tissue, muscle or bone, whatever is appropriate for YOU.

And if you are unsure of the path to prescribe you are giving your healing agent permission to find the best path that it can use and giving it permission to travel to the area and go to work.

From time to time, your special healing friend, agent or weapon is reporting back to you on the progress it is making. You are complimenting it for the good job it is doing and encouraging it to continue working on your behalf. Each time you do this the healing grows stronger and more powerful and you are concentrating your healing thoughts on any area in the body and your body, spirit and mind responds and your special healing agent becomes more powerful.

Each time your healing agent reports back to you, you are giving it further updated instructions. You may wish to speak to it softly in a relaxed manner, or you may hear yourself saying strong positive and expressive words. You may simply thank it for the good work that it is doing and encourage it to work longer hours in getting the job done. And your special healing agent, friend or weapon is working even harder and the particular part of your body is growing new defenses and revitalizing all the appropriate functions.

You are encouraging the healing process with understanding and patience and by simply closing your eyes the process magically begins and every time you close your eyes and allow the process to travel and work in any part of your body you are realizing and recognizing that the healing powers of your mind are stronger and more effective in each and every way.

Summary

The most important consideration in developing client-centered imagery is not what you say, rather what you don't say. The use of descriptive words that allow the subconscious mind to design its own unique and individual thoughts are preferred to those that direct a client to imagine a limited scene constructed by the therapist.

Imagery is the use of words to paint mental pictures. The words of the hypnotherapist are simply the tools that the subconscious mind employs to put an imagery painting onto the canvas of positive and creative outcomes.

Positive and affirmative suggestions are accepted and acted upon faster when the client is allowed to develop their own type of imagery in a unique and personal way.

5

Client-Centered Therapy for Contemporary Women

A significant component of the hypno-therapeutic process is the client's expectation of desired results prior to actually beginning a series of therapy sessions. Building the client's belief system and heightened expectation of desired outcomes generally begins during the clinical interview portion of their first visit with the therapist. This is a time when the prestige of the therapist and establishing rapport is of great importance. The prestige of the therapist or the way the client perceives and accepts the therapist's clinical expertise, involves more than a cursory review of the therapist's academic background and clinical training. The therapist's ability to genuinely understand the dynamics of the problem presented for hypno-therapy often becomes a pivot point in establishing rapport with the client. A client's expectation is also enhanced when she feels that the therapist not only understands the symptomology of her presenting complaint, but also understands how this symptomology impacts on her life.

It is not necessary to have an extensive background in psychology or medicine to bring to the therapy session an advanced level of empathy and human understanding of problems facing contemporary women. When viewed as a separate and distinct modality of therapy, it can be said that therapeutic hypnosis is not concerned with the practice of psychology nor should it be. However, an understanding of what an individual client is feeling, how stress is impacting on her life as she meets the demands of daily living is essential. Stress is a topic that could fill several volumes. Several chapters could be devoted to just defining types of stress. For this reason the term stress when used in this chapter will refer to unwanted experiences or feelings that have a negative or undesired effect.

A large number of contemporary women seeking hypnotherapy today are concerned with weight control or stress associated with being a single parent, working mother and wife or stress related to job or family situations. There are many myths about hypnosis and hypnotherapy and an equal if not larger list of myths about the problems of contemporary women and what they should do to solve them.

The Great Weight Lie

According to the statistics of the American Dietetic Association, there are over 1500 different diets for weight control and over 50% of American woman are on a diet at any given time. This may be attributed to advertising, especially in the so-called 'sunshine states,' that women must be thin to be admired and accepted. One of the myths about being overweight is that being thin is the potential cure-all to any problem that exists. These advertisements would have you believe that if someone loses weight, everything in her life will suddenly be fantastic, she can do anything, be anything, go anyplace and everybody in the world will love her. In other words, lose the weight and it will be a magical end to all the problems in life. It is said that 'Fat is not where it's at, thin is in'. This may be a catchy sounding advertising slogan but it has no place in client-centered therapy.

Another myth is the belief that finding the right diet will solve the problem of being overweight. There are countless numbers of diet books on the market today. It seems that almost anybody who can write a book has written a diet book. The titles entice would-be readers and each new diet usually claims to be the best. The one thing most diet books have in common is the myth of the 'quick fix.' This is not to say that diet books are not beneficial and useful, however consumers should be aware of the difference between a diet book and a food plan for living. During an informal survey conducted at over eaters support groups over a two-year period, it was found that diet books did not significantly help overweight people with their problem. Most people who were overweight already knew what they had to do to lose weight.

Even the word diet has a negative meaning to many weight clients. One woman said she objected to the word diet because the first three letters spell "DIE." Another woman objected to the way the benefits of hypnosis were explained to her by a poorly trained hypnotist. Apparently this hypnotist insisted that overeating was the same kind of habit as smoking and that hypnosis would quickly remove the habit. This woman resented the implication that her problem was as simple as giving up cigarettes and stated, "What made him think that I could stop eating. If you never smoke another cigarette it won't kill you, but you can't just stop eating."

Client-centered therapy for people who have problems with permanent weight control must address the emotional and human dynamics of a compulsive personality in the area of food. Overeating is generally a manifestation or symptom of an underlying problem. You might say that overeating is filling a hole, filling a void where something is missing and the role of the therapist is to help that person discover the missing piece. It would be inappropriate for the therapist to delve into psychological issues and if these types of issues are significant, a referral to a psychologist is indicated. The therapist can help the client potentially find the missing piece by helping them to build their self-esteem. End result imagery may be used to help the client realize that they are needed and wanted by others and to accept and like themselves for who they are and what they are, not for what they think they look like or what others think they should be.

It is generally recognized today that overeating is a disease much the same as alcoholism is a disease. It is a blameless disease and not the result of a weak minded person or someone who lacks willpower. As with any disease, if untreated it gets worse like any disease process.

The idea that people who are overweight are lazy is another myth of the 'Great Weight Lie.' Low self-esteem might well be the result of working or trying too hard to be accepted by others. Oftentimes the overweight person has been put down most of her life in one way or another and has come to feel that she is a lesser person. Someone who is overweight can do and accomplish as much as anybody else, but after years of society often ignoring their positive accomplishments, it is hard for them not to internally accept that they are in fact 'lesser than' and in fact can't do and therefore self-esteem is deflated and they settle for less than they should.

The first step in therapy is to work with feelings of low self-esteem and stress that may be associated with these feelings. Examples of different types of stress that may be experienced by people who are overweight can be found in almost any daily activity.

Imagine an overweight person going shopping with a friend. They have decided to stop at a clothing store featuring the latest styles. As they walk into the store together the overweight person realizes that they cannot buy anything in that store, they need to go into the 'larger sizes' store.

She begins to worry about feeling embarrassed and what to say to her friend if the suggestion is made that she try on an outfit. Then the friend finds a dress and says "I love this outfit, it would look great on you, do you want to try it on?" Embarrassment now turns to stress as the overweight person swallows her real feelings. Rather than saying, "No, that's not my size," she may reply, "No, I don't like that." The significant stress factor for the overweight person in this situation is feeling that she always has to lie and deny to the world around her. This denial then becomes a part of her belief that she is what she is. Denial then becomes another form of stress as she realizes that denial is really lying to herself.

Another illustration of stress encountered by the overweight person is traveling on a plane or public transportation. Anyone who has traveled on a wide body plane knows that they do not come equipped with wide body seats. The person who weighs over 200 pounds would rather find another mode of transportation than squeeze into a seat and politely try to confine their body between two arm rests so as not to disturb another passenger.

Financial stress is also part of being overweight. Anything that is bigger generally costs more and this is no different for the person who is overweight. Queen size may be a polite term for extra large panty hose but they are not presented as gifts to a queen. You might even say they cost a king's ransom. Large women sizes in a clothing store also have a large size price tag. Then there are other costs for maintaining the oversized weight. This might include a wardrobe in different sizes so that they always have something to wear as their weight goes up and down from one diet or exercise program to the next. It can include the costs of dealing with emotional hunger pains that require more frequent eating or larger amounts of food. It may also include increased health care expenses for disorders related to being overweight.

Hypnotherapists who realize the underlying factors of stress associated with being overweight will want to avoid developing or using imagery that suggests a client see themselves participating in specific activities that have previously elicited stress associated with their weight problem.

The hypnotic formula concept (H=E+I+B+C) postulates that the process can move in two directions. One direction is from expectation to conviction that a change has occurred and future changes will continue to occur. The other direction is the opposite. Conviction is reversed when the spiral of belief is not built and maintained with a sequential series of positive, end result imagery suggestions. Positive words, thoughts and suggestions are the suggestions of choice within the concept of this formula. Another aspect of this concept is that two positives compound to produce more positives and a positive attached to a negative may cancel out the positive and reverses the formula.

An example of the positive suggestion linked to a negative experience resulting in frustrating results for a weight client can be found in excerpts from imagery presented on a cassette for weight loss and given to participants in a high volume and guaranteed results weight control program.

"Now see yourself going into a store and picking out a dress that is a smaller size and trying it on."

The overweight client has probably tried on many dresses smaller than her actual size with disappointing results and has negative memories about buying clothes in a smaller size.

"See yourself on a beautiful beach wearing a lovely and attractive two-piece bathing suit and you are the weight you want to be."

The client may have negative feelings about being seen on a beach in any type of bathing suit.

"Now see yourself standing in front of a dressing room mirror and putting on an outfit that is the size you want to be and it feels good doesn't it? Now change the picture and see yourself going to the rack with large sizes, and how does that feel, and you realize you wouldn't trade the feelings of a smaller size back for the clothes on a large rack."

This imagery attempts to invoke a positive affirmation to continue working toward a desired outcome but in reality introduces the suggestion of failure and an aversion to more appropriate sizes.

In all of the above examples the imagery, though well-intentioned is dictated by one person to another who is expected to 'swallow it' and lose weight.

Client-centered therapy accepts the fact that being overweight is a disease process and a blameless disease process. Stress and guilt are predisposing factors and often inhibit the healing process. Imagery used in helping weight clients must be formulated to avoid compounding feelings of past guilt and allow the client to forgive themselves for human mistakes and move forward. It is also important that the client come to understand and realize that taking one small step forward can be more beneficial than trying to take a giant step with a 'quick fix' diet or setting new unrealistic goals.

People who are overweight are often angry at themselves for being overweight and anger is an emotion that turned inward produces guilt. Unhealthy anger and guilt in turn reduces a person's sense of self-esteem and self-worth. Imagery that allows the client to take off the burdens of life, imagery that is relaxing and non-directive can produce instant emotional weight loss. Losing the weight requires a new food plan for living with a proper balance between 'food for thought' to meet emotional needs as well as food to maintain physical health.

Many people who overeat are angry at themselves. They eat to suppress their anger and their feelings for life in general. They are angry at themselves, angry at the world around them, angry at people who perceive them one way when they are not that way at all and angry that they cannot stop overeating and blaming everyone else around them for the way that they feel. You might say that feelings of anger actually create a larger emotional void in the overweight person that requires them to push down even larger amounts of food to fill the hole that continues to become deeper and wider. Oftentimes anger is suppressed because the overweight person feels that if the anger ever comes out they will literally explode.

Another myth of the great weight lie is that overweight people are funny and have a great sense of humor. Many people think an overweight person can always bounce back, like a bull running through a china shop and then wagging its tail at the end of a cartoon while the star of the cartoon laughs and says "That's all, doc." Overweight people are not necessarily anymore humorous or funny than anyone else. They may be perceived as funny by society because they generally are people pleasers. They tend to do anything for anybody so that others will like them. The overweight person often attempts to be an over-achiever in order to supply that missing something to their feelings of low self-esteem and self-worth. Realizing the exceptional qualities of the overweight person will enable the therapist to help the client turn hidden assets into visible rewards. The rewards of enhanced self-worth and self-image are more emotionally filling and produce longer lasting results than the best diet plan available.

Another myth in the 'Great Weight Lie' is, the overweight person who loses weight only to gain it back just hasn't found the right diet or went through the wrong weight loss program and this time things will be better. The truth of the matter is that every time someone attempts to lose weight and then gains it back lowers their self-esteem and belief that they can accomplish their goal. This may be termed the Yo-Yo effect. When a counselor in a weight program or any person the client perceives to be knowledgeable, tells a client that they will lose the weight and they guarantee it, they are potentially establishing an unfulfilled expectation on the part of the client. When the client begins to gain some of the weight back, they often feel even more frustrated. This frustration can then decrease their already low sense of self-worth and self-esteem and make it even harder for them to lose weight the next time.

One need only to watch the many ads on television or in the newspaper for weight loss programs to realize how many of the claims made in the ads are a type of hypnotic suggestion. When the client responds to these ads they have a heightened sense of expectation about the results no matter how unrealistic the results might be for the given client. Unfortunately their expectation is centered on the claims of the program and not centered in their own consciousness. Hypnotherapists know that permanent change in any unwanted behavior or habit must begin from within and grow from within. Hypnotherapists also know that for change to be permanent, the client must be given something they can use to help them for a lifetime rather than a method that teaches information and then leaves the student on their own.

Client-centered hypnosis is particularly effective for permanent weight control because it teaches clients how to develop new emotions and coping tools that they can use for life. In client-centered therapy, weight loss is not the goal or really even the most important aspect of therapy. Client-centered hypnotherapy addresses developing an attitude change and building a belief system. The goal of client-centered therapy is to help the client see themselves for what they really are and believe in themselves.

A Food Plan For Living

Developing a food plan for living with client-centered hypno-therapy begins during the first contact or conversation with the weight client. This contact may be over the telephone as a result of an advertisement or a referral. What you don't say during the conversation often produces longer lasting therapeutic results than assurances that the client will lose weight.

The therapist should emphasize that since being overweight is a symptom of many different underlying factors, the therapy program will be designed to meet the client's individual needs, stress factors, anxiety and tension that may be contributing to their problem. However, there is no guarantee that they will lose a certain number of pounds in a certain time period or that by completing a program in hypnotherapy they will have no desire to overeat. The desire to overeat is a result of other stress and anxiety factors. Therefore what the program can do for them is to teach them new ways to deal with problems they feel are responsible for their being overweight and teaching them techniques they can use for a lifetime to maintain the level of physical and emotional health they want to have. It should be emphasized that the objective of the program is to teach them skills for a new way of living, not how to lose pounds or stay on a diet.

During the first office consultation or therapy session with the weight client, the therapist may wish to establish some realistic expectations on the part of the client. These expectations should focus on feelings rather than pounds to lose. The client should also realize that to expect the therapist to do a 'quick fix' is a myth of the great weight lie. In other words, you are a good teacher, you understand and empathize with the feelings that are contributing to their weight problem but they are the one who creates the changes and they have the talent and ability and knowledge to make it happen.

You may wish to outline an initial series of learning sessions focusing on the various stress factors associated with the client's weight problem followed by therapy sessions addressing new ways of eating. Since overeating is also a disease of isolation, you may wish to provide the client with information about self-help groups in the local area. Attendance at self-help meetings will reinforce individual therapy and give the client someone to talk to other than the hour they spend with the therapist once a week.

The initial therapy session should be devoted to teaching the client a simple method for self-hypnosis relaxation. One technique that is easy for most clients to learn quickly is the 'Magic Spot' induction or 'Safe Place' imagery. The client can be taught these techniques by including the imagery during a progressive relaxation induction and relaxation imagery and giving post hypnotic suggestions that they can relax as deep as they are in the therapy session any time they choose to do so. Before the client leaves your office have them practice their self-induction and encourage them to use this tool for a new way of living daily until their next visit. The therapist may also want to provide a reinforcement *cassette* for them to listen to at home.

Underlying stress factors contributing to the overweight problem can be explored during the second therapy session. Hypnotherapy and especially client-centered hypnotherapy is not the practice of psychology and for this reason the most beneficial way to help a client discover hidden feelings of guilt and stress is to use a non-directive approach. Non-directive hypno-therapeutic suggestions should be formulated so that the client can become in touch with the feelings they wish to remember after they are alerted and not forced to recall feelings that they do not wish to deal with. The following imagery script is an example of non-directive suggestions that may enable a client to identify a given stress factor or factors associated with their problem.

And as you continue going even deeper relaxed and doing so very well now, so comfortable and so very relaxed, let yourself and allow yourself to wander easily through a library of feelings that are associated with being overweight. When you see a title that has meaning for you or a title that you wish to remember, open the book and look at the information that you choose. And you are looking at information and titles about the stress, tension, anxiety and feelings that you would like to change. And you are remembering only the information that you want to remember at this time in this place and information that is beneficial to you. You are ignoring the titles and information that you choose to ignore and looking for only the titles or information that you want to work with today. It is not necessary for you to visualize the title or information. You may be hearing it on a cassette or simply know what the title and information is you want to work with today.

You are realizing that you cannot check out every title and bit of information in the library and there is no need to do so. You are selecting a few titles and only the information you want to use today. Now picture and imagine that you are taking the information you want from the memory banks of your subconscious mind to the check out desk of your conscious awareness. You are selecting only the titles that you wish to bring to your conscious awareness.

Now let each title you want to work with represent a feeling or situation or circumstance that is associated with your problem of being overweight. And you are recognizing and realizing what is causing the stress or anxiety. The title may represent an experience on the job, in the home, with friends or others or just feelings of stress, anxiety or tension that seem to come and go. And picking or choosing one feeling of stress and giving it a first name. Stress is a last name, Job is the first name of Job Stress and Money is the first name of Money Stress and Self is the first name of Self-blame and Anger is the first name of Anger Stress.

When I alert you in a few moments you are sharing only the titles you want to work with in this time and this place and putting all the other titles back on the library shelf to look at at another time when you are relaxed and peaceful and as calm as you are now. You are talking about and sharing only the titles that you want to use to learn new skills for living in a relaxed and peaceful manner.

After alerting the client, ask them if there is something associated with their feelings of being overweight that they would like to work with using self-hypnosis. Ask them to be specific, i.e., job related stress, family stress, anger, procrastination, self-esteem or feelings of guilt. The areas they identified can be alleviated using appropriate imagery outlined in the chapter on Therapeutic Imagery.

It is important to remember that the role of the hypnotherapist in client-centered hypnotherapy is that of a guide and not that of a psychotherapist. It is wise to resist offering any kind of advice or observation about the client's feelings other than they are emotions expressed by a worthwhile person. If the client has grave reservations about the feelings that surfaced or is insisting on an interpretation, this is a client who needs psychological counseling in addition to hypnotherapy for vocational and avocational self-improvement.

The hypnotherapist may wish to schedule one or two more sessions to teach the client how to use imagery for the various areas of stress the client feels is a part of their weight problem and then continue with positive end result imagery of 'Thinking Thin.' It should be noted that thinking thin does not mean weighing thin. A great many overweight people have let thinking fat invade their feelings and inner sense of emotional well-being. The degree that someone is thinking fat is measured in pounds. Thinking thin is trading the wasted thoughts of fat for the wanted thoughts of a new, happy, peaceful and relaxing attitude about life and living. Thinking thin is measured by moments of time devoted to happy thoughts and a feeling of contentment and self-acceptance.

The number of sessions devoted to initial training in self-hypnosis and the various stress factors contributing to the client's problem with weight will be different for each individual. Some clients may experience dramatic results while others work longer to alleviate the causes of their problem associated with stress. Other clients may experience frustration and difficulty that may be concomitant with a medical problem. If a client expresses concern about not being able to lose more weight after several therapy sessions, the hypnotherapist should arrange for a medical consult so that the client can be evaluated for medical factors that may be inhibiting their weight loss. If the client is moderately overweight, has experienced weight loss during therapy and is not losing additional weight, they may have reached a normal and natural physical plateau.

The body habituates to any prolonged condition in an attempt to establish homeostasis. Homeostasis is an equilibrium or balance of all body functions. For instance, if the body is overloaded with water, the kidneys produce more urine or the sweat glands open up. If the body is low on water a pebble placed in the mouth will allow the salivary glands to make more moisture for the mouth and help satisfy the sense of thirst. Another example is a noise that occurs on a regular basis. A given sound that only happens occasionally alerts the fight or fright system (autonomic nervous system). This noise might be a passing train, the sound of an automobile horn or the chime of a grandfather clock while we are sleeping in a place that is not our home. If the sounds that stimulate our nervous system are repeated on a regular basis, the body recognizes that there is no need to become alarmed and turns down the arousal level of the sounds in the command center of the nervous system to bring the arousal system or fight or flight system back into balance (homeostasis). Homeostasis is the reason people who live near a railroad track seldom wake up with the passing of a train, or people who have a grandfather clock in their home seldom hear it chime when they are sleeping.

Homeostasis is also responsible for the body losing weight for a period of time and then maintaining a given weight despite the efforts to lose more weight. Obviously this is an over-simplification of human physiology, but it offers a conceptual explanation of the physical plateau in weight loss.

In any weight loss program, reduced caloric intake, exercise and appropriate attitude change and motivation interact to produce weight loss. The first weight to go is water weight and the last weight to go is stored body fat. This is due to the defense mechanism of the body or homeostasis.

The weight client who is healthy, motivated and learning to deal with stress factors in their life can be reassured through a plateau period with the following imagery.

A New Level of Success

You are reaching a new plateau and continuing to grow and create lasting change in your life. This plateau is a normal and natural resting place for your body. You are recognizing and realizing the special meaning this plateau has for you. You are relaxing and enjoying this marvelous, refreshing and resting place and feeling good about yourself. You are thinking thin and enjoying all the parts of you that are beautiful. These parts may be inside feelings and thoughts that satisfy you or they may be small changes in attitude or your sense of self-worth that is adding value to each and every aspect of your daily living.

Picture and imagine you are taking a walk or hiking through a wonderful valley, forest or mountain landscape or anyplace that is relaxing and comfortable. When you need to rest you are stopping in a shady spot under a tree or next to a stream or maybe just resting a moment on the side of a path or road. This resting place is a new plateau in your food plan for living. You are resting in a friendly spot, a comforting spot and relaxing and enjoying all the feelings of fresh air, clean healthy air and looking forward to continuing your journey to the next resting plateau. Now notice all there is to see, hear, smell, taste, touch and feel on this plateau that is enjoyable, satisfying and fulfilling. You are feeling confident, enjoying positive change and letting the human mistakes of the past melt away like flakes of snow in the warm springtime sun.

You are recognizing and realizing that as you rest on this plateau, the weight may stay the same for awhile and that's OK. You are simply at a resting place and it is a natural and normal time of resting for your body and your emotions and feelings. You are thinking thin and are proud of yourself. You are eating only the amount of food and the kinds of food that you know are necessary to maintain your good health. Your body is resting and you are enjoying a new sense of purpose, direction and well-being. You are enjoying a wonderful fulfilling sense of accomplishment, self-worth and personal pride. You are strong, healthy, loving and lovable and other people admire and respect this and enjoy being with you.

As you rest on this plateau, you are taking time to praise yourself for what you have accomplished so far and are realizing that perfection in all you do is not as important as living life one step at a time, one day at a time and enjoying a new plateau. You are giving yourself permission to reward yourself with happy, positive and healthful thoughts as you rest at this plateau and you are formulating and updating realistic goals to guide you to the next plateau in your food plan for living.

And you are giving your body and mind permission to use up the stored weight that you no longer need, want or desire. This might be emotional weight of stored up guilt and anger or the physical weight of stored up food you no longer need to feel good. And you are eating only the type of food and the amount of food that you know is good for you and filling up so much faster and enjoying life more and more and relaxing in preparation for the next step or plateau in your food plan for living.

Picture and imagine now that you are moving forward and continuing your walk or hike and as you leave this plateau the path becomes even more satisfying and more relaxing and you are walking with a new sense of well-being. And every time you leave a plateau you have increased energy, vitality and are refreshed and rejuvenated more than you have ever known yourself to be. There is no need to hurry as you continue to walk one step at a time.

Each step and each passing moment is more satisfying and more rewarding and you are eating food that is colorful and balanced. Your body is balanced and you are eating food that is rewarding and nutritious for your body and mind. You are filling your emotions with positive and rewarding thoughts and rewarding yourself by giving your body and mind time to rest and relax

And continuing your walk you are meeting new and worthwhile friends and guides. Your friends and guides are a part of you. They may be parts within you or friends you have known in the past or new friends that you are making now. You are no longer alone and you are enjoying every moment of every day in a new and different way. You are filling up on the joy of new self-esteem, self-worth, self-satisfaction and a new attitude about yourself and others.

You are a loving and caring person, you are loving and caring of yourself and you are loving and caring of others and for this reason other people love and care about you and respect you for the marvelous person that you are.

A weight client who learns self-hypnosis techniques for various contributing factors to their weight problem will usually be able to determine when therapy sessions should be terminated. This may be the end of formal hypnotherapy training, however, it should be viewed by the hypnotherapist as the beginning of a life-long process.

When other programs dismiss the student or participant, hypnotherapy can be a lifelong resource for the client. The therapist can reinforce the spiral of belief and changes the client has accomplished by providing a realistic follow-up program .

Rather than offering free visits or free group sessions or some other sales-oriented gimmick that the frustrated client seldom uses, a library of continuing education for weight loss can help the client meet new life situations in a more appropriate manner and maintain their emotional and physical weight loss. This continuing education library should include recorded self-improvement cassettes for the many problems that the weight client may experience in the future. The cassettes may be provided on a home rental basis or for use in the therapist's office at a nominal fee. During times of stress, knowing that there is a friendly place to go and a friendly voice to hear can be more comforting than sitting home alone and remembering past failures and mistakes. Oftentimes a weight client who has achieved success while working with a therapist is reticent to go back to the therapist and tell them that they need help again. A cassette library in the office that can be used by the client without having to explain a new situation or weight gain to the therapist can provide continuing support and may alleviate the client's feelings of low self-esteem or feelings of failure.

Reinforcement cassettes can be recorded by the therapist. The therapist can record a basic relaxation induction and follow this with imagery presented in this book and then add a standard awakening procedure. Each cassette should deal with only one therapeutic objective.

The continuing education library should also include a current list of self-help support meetings of various organizations in the local area that work with a variety of problems ranging from overeating to parents without partners and including but not limited to community social and recreational groups and activities

Being overweight is a disease process that can be arrested with proper intervention and therapy. However, it is also a disease of isolation. It is not enough to break the circle of contributing factors such as loneliness, stress, low self-worth and low self-esteem, the therapist must also guide the client towards new solutions and ways to continue developing a food plan for living.

The Super Woman Syndrome

Another aspect of client-centered hypnotherapy for contemporary women is stress associated with the super woman syndrome. This syndrome is predisposed by society's apparent emphasis that successful women must be everything, be able to do everything and be good at everything to win praise and recognition. These feelings of stress may be as prevalent with a homemaker as they are with a career woman.

Being a homemaker can be a stressful situation from time to time, however, many women today are not only a homemaker, they are also a working wife and mother or a single parent trying to fill the role of both a father and a mother. In these situations the contemporary woman can often feel overwhelmed and prolonged high levels of stress begin to take a toll on their physical and emotional health. This is an area where hypnotherapy can be extremely helpful.

Low self-esteem and a sense of failure may be the most significant contributing factor in the super woman syndrome. One need only to be cognizant of modern advertising to realize that an undue amount of importance is placed on women who are fashionable, beautiful and always in the news. The women who are athletes, who appear on talk shows or participate in high technology careers are often seen as being better than the homemaker who juggles budgets daily, is an expert in food preparation and family fashion and has developed a system for adding extra hours to an already overcrowded day. Today's working mother and wife seldom receives the praise she deserves and often may feel inferior and unappreciated. A wife and mother who is able to devote full time to taking care of a family may even feel guilty because they "just" stay at home.

Helping the client to realize her real value and contributions to society as well as her family is the first step in dealing with the stress associated with the super woman syndrome. In the case of the single woman, the term family can be expanded to include a close circle of friends or neighbors. This can be facilitated in hypnotherapy by having the client picture and imagine all the things they enjoy about her home or family circle. When someone is carrying a heavy burden of stress associated with her home, she may feel like her home is a confining situation or even like a jail cell and forget to take a few relaxing moments to enjoy what she has already accomplished.

When developing stress reduction imagery for the working wife and or mother, the therapist should take into consideration that this type of client actually has three full time jobs and each one includes a different set of stress factors. Rather than developing imagery under an umbrella title of stress, the therapist may wish to break the various stress factors down into categories of stress experienced at home, on the job or those that are a result of maintaining a home and a job. This approach is highly indicated for the client who is feeling stressed because she has been trying to do too many things at once.

Although many women pride themselves on being able to accomplish 36 hours of work in a 24 hour day, there are others who suddenly find that no matter how creative they are with time management they fall behind no matter what they do. The more they demand of themselves and expect of themselves the farther behind they get and a feeling of failure and frustration adds even more stress to an already stressful situation. The stress of different activities coupled with unfulfilled expectations creates self-doubt, self-criticism and self-blame. This becomes a circle of self-defeating anger that when directed inward becomes guilt and the process continues to gain momentum and become more disruptive in their activities of daily living. A client-centered and non-directive type of intervention is illustrated in the following imagery.

Super Woman Stress Intervention

And as you continue relaxing and feeling so very comfortable and relaxing even deeper down you are learning a simple technique to alleviate moments of unwanted stress in your life. You are also realizing that some amount or degree of stress is a necessary part of your life and actually helps you set goals and objectives and is a protection mechanism for your body, spirit and mind. So you are concentrating now on unhealthy stress and breaking it down into categories. And as you think of the unwanted stress in your life in terms of categories the circle of stress you are feeling now seems to dissolve into smaller parts that can be dealt with in an easier way with more effective and positive results.

Picture and imagine that you are previewing a film or flipping through the pages of a magazine and paying attention to one area of stress in your life. This might be the stress you feel while working at home, or the stress of a job or the stress of trying to do too many things at the same time. And you are alleviating this stress by picking out one item, incident or circumstance that you can work with now at this time and in this place and relaxing more and more and allowing the knots and tangled threads to unravel as you enjoy a marvelous nap.

And you are giving yourself permission to take this special nap because you are busy and realize that this five-minute nap will enable you to be as refreshed as if you had five hours of sleep and a five-minute break is an investment in increased vigor, vitality and productivity. Before you begin your relaxing and special nap you are taking a moment or two to select one feeling of stress that you want to dissolve and let float away or drift away while you relax.

This might be a feeling about an actual person, place or thing or a feeling that is upsetting to you or a feeling that you want to understand in a new and different way. There is no need to work at this feeling, just knowing it is there is OK.

Now closing your eyes and taking a few deep lung filling and relaxing breaths and every time you exhale relaxing more and more and the feeling is but a passing moment or thought in a pleasant relaxing daydream. All the negative and unwanted parts of the feeling or thought seem to float away like the water vapor from a pot on the stove or the morning fog lingering on a mountain top as you begin a marvelous five-minute, five-hour nap. And you are creating new ways of dealing with situations and new creative ways of accomplishing tasks and new and powerful ways of designing and making emotional and physical health free of unwanted and unnecessary anxiety, tension and stress.

And you are beginning your nap by setting an alarm clock that will alert you in exactly five minutes. This clock may have large easy to read numbers, sound an inspiring alarm or simply tell you when five minutes has passed. And you are setting the clock and watching the hands and going even deeper relaxed and enjoying the relaxation as deep as you are now in this time and in this place. And picturing and imagining now that you are in a very wonderful, magical and marvelous refreshing place. This special place may be at the beach on a private inlet or nestled in a mountain valley or a place in your home or anywhere else that is filled with happy, peaceful and relaxing thoughts and memories. And as you go even deeper relaxed, you are enjoying all the things there are to touch, sense, smell, see and hear that make this place so very relaxing and tranquil. And going there now and enjoying this place until the alarm clock you have set alerts you. You are enjoying a marvelous five-minute, five-hour nap and the stress is drifting and fading and new creative and innovative thoughts are becoming more and more powerful as you relax even deeper.

And you are awakening normally and naturally at the exact time you have set on the clock. And you are more refreshed than you have ever known yourself to be. You are feeling as if you have been sleeping peacefully and deeply for five hours and only five minutes have passed. And with each five-minute nap you are relaxing even deeper and the stress of a given situation, problem or unwanted feeling is fading and floating away and being replaced with a new sense of accomplishment and direction. Even the little thoughts during a daydream are working in your life and you are recognizing that perfection is not as important as taking time to relax and using new information to solve small problems one at a time rather than taking on a giant task and worrying about the outcome.

And you are taking this revitalizing and refreshing nap any time you desire to do so by simply closing your eyes, taking a few deep relaxing breaths and picturing and imagining a favorite or safe place. And every time you do this there is more to see, hear, smell, touch and enjoy in your safe place and it becomes more vivid in your mind's eye.

Since this favorite safe place is of your own design and choosing you may let others share it with you or you may keep it a secret, private place and you are enjoying this place in a way that is the most appropriate and most relaxing for you.

And setting the clock to alert you in exactly five minutes and enjoying this place and new discoveries and new thoughts of feeling good and opening your eyes and so refreshed in exactly five minutes.

───────────────────■───────────────────

This imagery should be presented to a client during a hypnotherapy session. After alerting the client in a traditional manner, it is suggested that the therapist have the client practice setting the clock in her mind's eye and returning to her safe place. Once the client demonstrates that she can induce self-hypnosis and return to her favorite or safe place, she should be encouraged to practice this technique on a daily basis and at other times when she feels unwanted stress in any given situation or circumstance.

PMS—Premenstrual Syndrome

There are a variety of definitions of premenstrual syndrome and a current debate of the etiology emphasizing both a psychogenic (emotional) cause and a physical cause. The scientific controversy and physiological aspects of this syndrome are beyond the scope of this chapter and are not necessary considerations for understanding the application of client-centered hypnotherapy for women who are affected by problems associated with PMS. The therapist need only recognize that the symptoms of PMS may range from minor physical or emotional discomfort to feelings of deep depression that may include thoughts of suicide. Clients who are suffering from PMS should be carefully evaluated before beginning a program of hypnotherapy. If profound psychological or medical symptoms are concomitant with other stress factors, it is wise to request a medical and psychological consult.

Some of the symptoms of PMS that may be alleviated with hypnotherapy include:

- Extreme moodiness before, during or after menstrual period.
- Easily upset by minor problems.
- Crying for no particular reason.
- Feelings of light despair.
- Experience minor to migraine headaches
- Experience bloating.
- Experience severe cramping in the abdominal area or extremities during menstrual cycle.

What is important for the therapist to remember is that the symptoms of PMS are very real for the client and should not be dismissed as a simple psychosomatic problem. Oftentimes the emotional factors of PMS are more important than the physical symptoms.

Emotional problems related to stress can be alleviated with relaxation imagery and end result imagery for specific stress problems the client is experiencing These problems may include anger, guilt, low self-esteem, nervous tension and anxiety.

Physical complaints such as headache, low backache, sensitive breasts or leg cramping can be alleviated with 'Pain or Anxiety As The Object' imagery. This type of imagery is presented in the chapter on Therapeutic Imagery. 'The Protective Shield' is another type of imagery that can be used with the PMS client.

A combination of physical and emotional complaints may be alleviated with imagery for a 'Five-Minute, Five-Hour Nap' presented in this chapter.

Summary

Various factors of stress significantly impact on the problems of contemporary women. These stress factors may contribute to problems with weight control and low self-esteem.

An advanced level of understanding and empathy for the human dynamics of the overweight client can potentiate the desired therapeutic outcome and enable the therapist to develop more effective client-centered imagery.

External stress manufactured by modern society and internal stress associated with the Super Woman Syndrome can be alleviated by working with one category of stress rather than working with a myriad of stress factors that are contributing to the client's immediate problem.

The symptoms of PMS should be divided into two general categories, emotional and physical. Emotional problems can be ameliorated with imagery that enhances self-esteem, self-worth and relaxation. Physical symptoms can be alleviated with imagery for pain management. PMS clients with profound and remarkable symptoms should be referred to a physician or psychologist for evaluation and consultation before continuing therapy.

6

Hypnotherapy for Children

Today's highly technological and competitive society often inhibits a child's ability to operate at their full potential. Youngsters today face a growing number of pressures and demands that can adversely affect their motivation, sense of self-esteem and ability to alleviate stress and relax in a variety of situations related to school, family and community life.

Low self-esteem is a significant factor in problems experienced by children who are having difficulties in school, in family situations or sports activities. Children are highly suggestible and even an off-hand remark can decrease a youngster's sense of self-esteem or self-worth. A child who is teased and told that he or she is stupid or clumsy may well act on the unintended remark and begin acting clumsy or stupid. A child who is admonished to perform at peak proficiency in a sports event or classroom exercise may feel extremely tense, nervous and anxious. The inability to break the feeling of tension may lead to a sense of frustration and an even greater feeling of nervousness and lower self-esteem. Oftentimes low-self esteem can be enhanced if just one person believes in a child and allows the child to create their own solutions to a given problem by believing in themselves. One person who can make a difference in the areas of low self-esteem, low motivation, enhanced concentration and memory is the client-centered hypnotherapist. The hypnotherapist can also provide a child with a life-long tool for alleviating inappropriate tension and anxiety.

Getting Acquainted

The initial meeting with a child is a much different situation than a pre-talk or clinical interview with an adult. An explanation of hypnosis, outline of the program the therapist intends to follow and the therapist's background is beyond the scope of understanding or beyond the scope of interest of most children. In many ways the child is really conducting the interview without using words and determining if the therapist is a person they will like or trust. The child may be asking silent questions such as; how boring will you be, are you a hard person to please, do you really like children and are you willing to let me try something my way?

It has been said that dog or cat has an instinct for knowing if you really like animals or are afraid of animals. This may also be said about children. They seem to instantly see through even the most elaborate disguises and quickly come to very simple conclusions about an adult or authority figure.

Since the child has already been told you are an important person by the parent or person responsible for bringing him or her to your office, the first step in the pre-talk or clinical interview is to let the child know you are willing to listen and willing to be their friend.

Pretend for a moment that you are a youngster who has been ushered into a hypnotherapist's office. You are not sure about what the hypnotherapist does but you have been told you have to go and to pay attention and act polite. The therapist smiles at you and then explains that you have to sit still, pay attention, do what you're told and then insists that you close your eyes in an unfamiliar and possibly even scary room. How are you reacting? You may be outwardly appearing to follow instructions and do what you're told while on the inside you are saying 'NO' to every suggestion offered.

Now pretend that you are a youngster who has entered an office and the therapist smiles, says hello and comes out from behind a big desk and sits down next to you. The therapist is a tall person but he doesn't seem to be so tall because he is sitting in a small chair and is just a little bit taller than you are. Rather than telling you what you are suppose to do, he asks your name and ask you if he can call you by that name or if you have a nickname you like better. He asks if he can get to know you better and tells you to call him by his first name. The questions the therapist asks are fun to answer because they are about things you like or things that are fun to do. When the therapist asks you what your favorite sport is or your favorite animal or the name of your best friend, he lets you talk without interrupting you or telling you that something you said is wrong or you shouldn't feel a certain way. How do you feel in this situation?

The above scenario is an illustration of a client-centered approach in establishing rapport with a child. The youngster who is experiencing problems that can be helped with hypnotherapy has more need for a new friend than another teacher, coach or person in authority telling them what to do.

Many times the hypnotherapist will use a permissive type of induction and imagery with adult clients who are authority figures such as physicians, lawyers or business executives. The rationale is that people who are accustomed to giving orders are more receptive to a permissive induction and inferred suggestions rather than an authoritative type of induction and direct suggestions. If this is the technique of choice for working with adults, then it would follow that the technique of choice when working with children is an authoritative and direct suggestion approach. This, however, is often counterproductive and builds resistance to therapy on the part of the youthful client.

Youngsters are generally very creative and develop a million and one let's pretend games and imaginary friends without any outside or external advice or instruction. Working with children may be the classic situation where what you say is of far less importance than what you don't say. This concept may be illustrated by imagining you are a child again and listening to the following suggestion.

Now let yourself pretend you are daydreaming and it's OK to close your eyes if you want, and pretend you are having a fun time in a magic place and when you open your eyes you can tell me how to get to this magic place and tell me something about this place that you want me to know.

A permissive approach coupled with inferred imagery suggestions may produce more surprising and dramatic results in establishing rapport than a traditional suggestibility test or soliciting an extensive case history from a child.

A young man was referred to my office by his parents who had labeled him a chronic liar and were frustrated by his persistent lying in spite of many different types of punishment and repeated visits to a counseling center. This young boy seemed to be overly anxious to please me and receive a good report that could be given to his parents. He was impressed with a model of a boat on my desk and began asking me questions about the boat and why I was interested in boats. As we talked, I told him about my experiences with sailing off the coast of California and how relaxing it was to enjoy an outing on my boat. When I asked him if he wanted to pretend we were going on a sailing trip together, he readily agreed. I suggested that we could both close our eyes and pretend we were getting on the boat and going for a boat ride together. On this trip he would be the captain and I would help him when he asked me to. When we got back to the dock and he opened his eyes he had found the solution to his problem.

During our sailboat daydream I asked the youngster where we were going. He described a hidden cove and I asked him how he knew we were going in the right direction. He said he had climbed to the lookout station and could see the cove off in the distance. I then asked him if he was sure we were going in the right direction. He replied, "That's something I wouldn't lie about." Later in our pretend journey he told me that his hands were sore from holding onto the steering wheel. I asked him if he wanted me to steer for awhile and he replied, "No I can steer, but I don't want to bite my nails anymore."

During our daydream sailing trip we had become good friends. This let's pretend game had become a way for the youngster to identify the real problem that frustrated him. The problem he wanted to work on, biting his nails. Apparently his parents often had loud discussions about money problems and seemed to be angry with each other a lot of the time. When asked a question that the young boy felt would start another argument, he invented a story he hoped would make things better. His frustrated attempts to solve an adult problem and low self-esteem created by being caught in untruthful explanations precipitated nervous tension and biting his nails. Since he was at an age where children who bite their nails are often ridiculed and poked at in fun by their peers, he saw the immediate problem as nail biting, not telling lies.

In subsequent therapy sessions we often took a daydream sailing trip together and his fingernails grew to a strong and healthy length as we steered through dangerous reefs and discovered far off islands together. As his fingernails began to look the way he wanted them to, he took new pride in his appearance and conduct at school. On one occasion when his parents confronted him about some ice cream missing from the family refrigerator, he replied that he had eaten it because he was feeling lonely and was afraid to interrupt them to ask if it was OK because they were fighting. This one admission triggered a new beginning in his relationship with his parents.

The important point for the client-centered hypnotherapist to remember is that by spending time developing a friendly rapport with a child often produces results that are longer lasting than determining what the therapist perceives the problem to be and insisting that since we are adults, adults know best. When working with children, the attitude of "Father knows best" or "Do what I say" only creates resistance and negative expectations on the part of the youthful client.

Another important consideration in establishing rapport with a child is avoiding the tendency to talk down to them or trying to be too friendly, too soon and too fast. A youngster is taught that he has to follow the orders of their parents, he has to obey the orders of a teacher and he is also taught that he can say no to a friend, have an argument and go home crying and then come outside the next day and the friend is still there. How marvelous that childhood battles are quickly forgotten between children and how unfortunate that when the battle is a confrontation between a child and an adult it is often long remembered. The way a child remembers their initial meeting with a therapist can make the difference in the outcome of their therapy many years later.

A child has his own sense of identity and privacy and can be as resentful as an adult of someone who invades his private world of thoughts and feelings without being given permission to do so. The child may not be able to articulate his inner feelings on an adult level but he does know what he doesn't like and what makes him uncomfortable. An eight-year-old with a prodigious vocabulary and an outgoing vivacious personality may suddenly withdraw and be at a loss for words when questioned by a substitute teacher about what he has been learning in class. This may also be true for a six-year-old who still believes in Santa Claus but is forced to sit on the lap of a man in a Santa Claus suit at a local department store. The need to protect his private thoughts, feelings and sense of space is as important to a youngster as it is to an adult.

As an adult we often have a conversation with someone we respect as an authority figure. Consider a situation where you are asking a doctor to explain a given medical condition and what he is prescribing to help you alleviate the problem. If the doctor said he was prescribing a pink pill and a blue pill and you should take them before saying your bedtime prayers, you would probably feel incensed that he used such childish terms. If he said he was prescribing (a name you have never heard of pill) for muscle tension and another medication (you have never heard of) and you should take them before going to bed, you would feel more confident in his ability and management of your problem even though you did not remember or understand the medical name of the pills. This is also true for the child who presents for hypnotherapy. "I am going to show you a way to relax and a technique for improving your grades," will be better received than a comment such as, "We are going to play a daydream game and it will help you be a good listener in school."

Hypnotherapy is a learning process. The hypnotherapist is someone who is skilled at teaching others how to enter self-hypnosis and use their own abilities and understanding to achieve a desired outcome. The term "their own abilities" applies to any given level of learning or understanding and the level of under-standing and learning of a child is of equal importance as the level of understanding and learning of an adult. A client-centered hypno-therapist should take the opportunity to create an enhanced learning process by suggesting words that are learning tools rather than words that the therapist decides will be easily recognized by the child.

It is interesting to watch a group of youngsters interacting with each other and noting the vocabulary they use. Oftentimes the adjectives used in their discussions are more related to conceptual feelings rather than dictionary definitions. The expression, "I hate vanilla ice cream" does not necessarily mean that the child does not like vanilla ice cream. It can also mean they only like vanilla ice cream if there is chocolate syrup on top or it is served with a vanilla wafer or another kind of cookie. When in doubt as to what a child really means, ask them what they really mean and listen closely.

Allowing the child presenting for hypnotherapy to establish their own space in the therapeutic setting, will enhance the rapport between the child and the therapist. Space can be an emotional sense of distance or closeness as well as a physical distance or proximity. Though the term child generally refers to youngsters under 12 the term for therapeutic work can be expanded to those who are in their early teens. Spacial orientation is of equal importance regardless of the youngster's chronological age.

Younger children may feel more relaxed and comfortable if they can pick a chair that is near the door, off in a corner or a chair that they like, such as a rocking chair or even a piano stool that can swivel around as they talk. Older children may prefer to sit in a reclining chair, stretch out on an arrangement of pillows or even a couch.

Youngsters are unique in that they often bring their own preconceived notions and ideas to the therapy session. These ideas are often far from the mainstream of thinking and may not seem to be relevant to the therapist's clinical goals, but they are the beginning of successful child-centered hypnotherapy.

I was asked to see a high school student who was having problems as a result of his parent's divorce. He was doing poorly in his academic studies at school. His father brought him to the office so that I might help him improve his athletic performance as a place kicker on the high school football team and program him to work harder on his classroom homework assignments. After meeting with the youngster and his father and listening to the father's concerns, I asked to talk to the young man alone and began a program of therapy.

As soon as the father left the room, his son asked how I could help him since I didn't have a couch in my office. When I asked why I needed a couch he replied, "Because my father says a shrink can't help you unless you lay on a couch and listen to what he tells you." I took a few moments to explain that I was a hypnotherapist and not a "shrink" and that it was OK for him to sit in a chair and he could pretend it was a couch if that is what he wanted to do. When he told me he was planning to leave if he had to lay on a couch I knew we had established a degree of rapport. This young man had pre-conceived notions about what I was supposed to do and he had already decided to tune me out. When he realized that I was not another father figure and would not offer suggestions or attempt to help him by (his words) 'acting like a big shot.' we discovered that the reason he was doing poorly as a place kicker was due to a fear of heights he had never expressed to anyone and felt was a great character flaw. This sense of low self-esteem rapidly vanished as we explored the positive feelings of accepting things the way they are, rather than trying to change the things other people say would change if the youngster acted different and simply did what he was told.

During subsequent therapy sessions, this young man came to realize that he could relax in stressful academic or sport situations and learned a technique for focusing his attention and concentration on the immediate task at hand. His sense of self-esteem and self-worth improved as he took control of his own life and established goals that were meaningful to him. Some of these goals were; kicking the ball straight without blaming himself if it did not go far enough to make a score in a football game, consistently doing the best he could in class and completing homework assignments without judging his effort by his father's remarks of praise or criticism and learning new ways to improve his visual and auditory memory. His fear of heights was dissolved with non-directive therapy that enabled him to picture and imagine being successful and relaxing in various activities that took place on the top of high mountains and in a space lab far above the earth. Traditional desensitizing imagery was not used because this young man had already indicated the path he wished to follow to attain his goal of freedom from worry about failing in the eyes of others.

While getting acquainted with a youthful client the hypno-therapist should also pay attention to the immediate goals the client desires. The goals and desired outcomes expressed by parents may be noble aspirations for the child over a period of time, but not amiable to immediate intervention.

Building a spiral of belief and helping the child to become convinced that they have the ability to create wanted changes in their life is enhanced when therapy is directed to something that can happen in the near future or better yet, something that can happen in the next couple of weeks. The therapeutic outcome can also be directed at one specific outcome or expectation. When this outcome has become a reality it will enhance conviction that another outcome will also happen. The childhood game of 'Mother May I' is a good example of a therapeutic approach when working with children. Most anyone can take a small baby step in the learning process of living life to their maximum potential. Giant steps are harder to take and several baby steps may produce more positive results and forward momentum than one giant step.

Child-Centered Induction Techniques

Child-centered inductions can be classified in two general categories. Category one is for children between the ages of 6 to 10. Category two is for children 11 to 15. Children who are in their early teens may also respond well to creative inductions used with adults. The induction imagery presented in this chapter may be used as written or as a guide for developing a more meaningful script for an individual child.

Each script assumes that children have a fertile and vivid imagination and with a minimum of direction, will use their imagination to accomplish the feelings they want to experience in their own way. Permissive end result imagery is emphasized along with direct suggestions that outline the steps the child should take to reach a state of deep relaxation. It is not necessary for the child to understand the term hypnosis and the use of the word is often contraindicated if the child has seen movies depicting people in hypnosis who act strange or appear to be under the control of someone else.

The therapist may wish to begin work with a youngster using one type of induction imagery to see what will happen. Children are very inquisitive and their cooperation can often be heightened by giving them a choice of titles to try. For instance; "I would like to show you the "Sleepy Game" and the "Magic Star Game" so that you can see which one you like best. Which one should we start with?" The therapist may wish to offer an older child a larger choice. "I have a list of games and exercises we can work with today. They are the Sleepy Game, the Magic Star, the TV Show, Follow the Leader and the Blackboard Game. Which one would you like to learn?" When a child asks a question about a specific title, the therapist can give a short and simple explanation by way of demonstrating the imagery for the child to see what will happen.

For instance, if the child chooses an induction imagery title such as the "Sleepy Game" and wants to know more about it, the therapist can suggest that the youngster close his eyes and listens as the therapist explains it and then the child can decide if they like that game or want to choose another one.

This approach sets up enhanced cooperation and a curious imagination which can combine to facilitate misdirection of attention in the hypnotic formula.

The following induction imagery is for children in category one. The therapist may use one title or combine the imagery of several titles to induce a state of hypnosis.

The Sleepy Game

Now I am going to tell you about the sleepy game and you can play the game with me by looking at your pointer finger. You don't have to look at me just look at your pointer finger and wiggle it a little and as you watch your pointer finger it can become very sleepy. Close your eyes and pretend that your finger wants to take a nap and when I ask your finger if it is getting sleepy you can move it a little bit and pretend is it is getting very sleepy. If your finger moves a lot when I ask if it's sleepy it means it is still wide awake and you are telling it to be sleepy and it is paying attention and getting sleepy. And every time your finger moves it is getting more sleepy.

Maybe you are telling it a sleepy story or covering it with a blanket or putting it in a special place where it can feel sleepy and it's OK for the finger to take a nap. You are not getting sleepy or taking a nap, you are just playing the sleepy game and letting your finger take a nap for a couple of minutes and moving the finger. It feels so sleepy now and is starting to take a sleepy game nap. And you can pretend that you are playing the sleepy game. You are not really sleepy, just pretending, listening to me with your eyes closed and pretending you can't hear me because your finger is taking a nap. And your eyes want to play the sleepy game too and they are getting sleepy and don't want to open because when they are sleepy you listen better and have more fun playing the sleepy game. And you are playing the sleepy game with your best friend or your favorite person on TV or with a special person or animal you want to play the game with you. And your eyes are closed and sleepy because this is how we play the sleepy game. And we can start the game when your finger is so sleepy it doesn't want to move and trying to move it and feeling how sleepy your finger is. And your whole body wants to play the sleepy game and you are telling your body to be quiet and be sleepy and play the game and listening and pretending your body is sleepy and you feel good and the sleepy game is fun and you can play the game anytime you want to.

Note: Misdirection of attention was established by the child concentrating on a finger getting sleepy. The ideomotor movement of the finger is signaling the level of hypnosis. The child is pretending to nap or daydream and creating their own imagery of what this comfortable and relaxing place is like. The therapist can now continue with therapeutic imagery.

The Magic Star

Now we are going to make a magic star and all you have to do is close your eyes and listen to my voice and the voice of the star maker. And the voice of the star maker will speak in a few moments if you close your eyes and let yourself pretend that you are making a magic star and I am showing you how to do this as you listen to a story and at the end of each page you are turning the pages of the story book and soon you are making the magic star.

And what will the magic star be? You are keeping your eyes closed and waiting for the magic star. And the star can be something you are drawing on a piece of paper or something that you think a magic star should be or it can just be a magic star with magic lights and shapes and a magic voice that makes you feel happy and is helping you and your whole body is feeling good and you are pretending to be sleeping. And when I ask you if you are sleeping you are nodding your sleepy head and looking for the magic star with your eyes closed.

Every time you nod your head the magic star is getting closer and your head and your whole body feel more sleepy and this is OK as the magic star changes colors or sizes or shapes because it is your special magic star and only you can see, hear and feel the magic. And the magic makes you feel good and you can play with your magic star anytime you want to and you can listen to my voice and pretend you are sleeping and have fun with your magic star.

Now I want you to ask your magic star a question and the star can answer you. If the star says yes nod your head. Ask the star if you can pretend to be sleepy and your whole body is sleepy and feeling good. Nod your head . . . Now ask the star if it is OK for you to listen to the magic voice of the star and nod your head. Now you can find out a secret about the magic star, ask the star what color it is or ask the star to tell you its name, but don't say anything to me. This is your secret, the secret of the magic star and you can listen with your eyes closed and your whole body feeling sleepy and good.

Note: The magic star is a creation of the child's own imagination and is used to misdirect attention. Ideomotor signals can be observed with head movement to indicate the level of hypnosis. A post session discussion of the child's magic star can be used to aid the induction of hypnosis during the next therapy session.

The TV Show

Now I want you to close your eyes and listen for the sound of a click as I turn on a 'let's pretend' TV. Don't close your eyes real tight, just pretend you are keeping them closed and listen for the click. You can turn on the TV by yourself if your eyes are closed. As long as your eyes are closed you can watch the TV as long as you want and that's OK while your eyes are closed and what will come on the TV when we make it click on? Listen now and when you want to hear the click, nod your head, OK the TV is on and you can pretend to hear the sound, these are happy sounds and they make you feel good and you can feel sleepy if you want and listen to my voice and ignore all the other sounds and listening to my voice and the sound of the TV and I am going to say click and you can feel even more sleepy and see the TV better and watching a very special TV show. And click and now you can pick out your favorite show. When you turn the knob and change the picture nod your head and you are watching your favorite show. And click the picture is perfect now and you are watching this special TV and feeling so very relaxed and feeling good and ignoring everything except what is on the TV and the story I am telling you. And you are watching the TV and listening to me because your eyes are closed and your whole body is listening and watching because we can see and hear special things on your TV.

Now pretend that your favorite TV character is on the screen and you are thinking that they should be sleepy and as you watch them they are sleepy too and let them get real sleepy and feeling good and relaxed like you are and watch them get sleepy and relaxed like you and watch what they do and listen to what they say. If you don't hear them talking that's OK because they are too sleepy now just like you. They are not really sleeping, they are just pretending to feel sleepy like you are pretending to feel sleepy and your eyes are so sleepy they don't want to open and you are telling your eyes to feel sleepy so you can watch the TV and listen to a story and feel good and pretend you are playing a make believe game.

And we can change the channel now and look at another TV show and when I say click we have a new picture on the TV screen and we are having a lot of fun. And click, and now the picture is so easy to see and the sound is just right and you are ignoring everything except my voice and the new TV show.

Follow the Leader

Now pretend that you have been walking for a long time and it is time for you to close your eyes for just a few moments and sit down and rest and you feel like sounding like you are tired and make that sound for me. Now show me how you would look if you were really tired and wanted to go to sleep. Now close your eyes and pretend you are making a sound and showing me how sleepy you are. You can do it with your eyes closed because you are just pretending and we are playing a game and it's OK for me to be silly and for you to laugh.

In fact, the more you laugh and the more sounds you make the more fun the game is and keeping your eyes closed is part of the game. And the game is pretending to follow the leader. We are not going to really follow the leader, we are going to show the leader how to rest and relax so that you can move up to the front of the line and watch the leader make sleeping sounds while you discover the secrets the leader wants you to know. And this is how we tell the leader to sleep and daydream. First whisper to the first person in front of you and say deep sleep. Now watch them sit down and pretend to sleep. They are not really sleeping, they are just pretending to rest and they look very relaxed under a tree, at the side of a patch or maybe even in a chair someplace. Now you have to be very quiet and keep your eyes closed to make this happen and when the first person starts to take a nap, move up to the next person and say deep sleep. Each time you do this you are feeling more and more relaxed and sleepy and pretending to talk to the next person and the next person and each time you do you are getting close to the leader. I am going to count from one to five and on the number five you will be next to the leader, is that OK with you, nod your head please. OK, one, and you are more sleepy and relaxed and pretending and, two, very sleepy now and barely nodding your head, and three, hardly moving your head and so relaxed and closer to the leader and four, your head is so heavy and sleepy now and five, next to the leader and listening only to my voice and your head is so heavy and telling the leader, deep sleep and the leader sit down and you are listening to the secrets and your head is so heavy it doesn't want to move.

Note: This imagery allows the child to interact in both the conscious and subconscious states. The more he or she participates with their eyes open, the expectation of a fun game is reinforced. The more they participate with their eyes closed, the effect of Voight's fractionation of their laughter deepens the hypnotic state.

———————————■———————————

The Blackboard Game

To play this game you have to concentrate on what I am saying and close your eyes. The blackboard we are going to play the game on is like the one at school but you can only see it if your eyes are closed. So close your eyes for a couple of minutes and pretend you can see the blackboard as I tell you what I am writing on it.

On the top of the blackboard I am making a picture of an animal. Now this animal can be any animal you would like to pretend it is. Keep your eyes closed and watch me draw an animal you want to be on the blackboard. I have drawn the animal and when you pretend to see it nod your head. Very well, now next to your animal I am writing a number and it is any number you want it to be, when you see the number nod your head. OK, now I am writing the word sleep and it is easy to see the words or just know that the word is on the blackboard. Concentrate on the word sleep and when you eyes seem to be heavy and sleepy, nod your head. Very well, now you can pretend to erase a picture, number or word from the blackboard. Each time you erase something from the blackboard you are feeling more and more comfortable and your eyes are heavier and sleepy and you feel more relaxed.

Erase something from the blackboard and let yourself feel more relaxed and my voice is easy to listen to and all the other sounds are not important as you concentrate on the blackboard. Now go even deeper relaxed and erase something else that is on the blackboard. Concentrate on what you are erasing and do it slowly so that you are listening only to my voice as you erase it and now take your time and make the blackboard clean and erase anything that is still there. Erase everything that is still there so that when the blackboard is clean you feel very relaxed and are listening only to my voice and every word is relaxing you deeper and you are writing other things on the blackboard when you want to. And what are the other things you are writing or drawing? And these things are helping you to feel even more comfortable, sleepy, relaxed and learning a new game that is always fun to play and a game you can use anytime you want too.

Now when the blackboard is all clean and you are ready to make another picture, number or word, nod your head please.

Note: Ideomotor signals can indicate a level of hypnosis as well as the child's willingness to accept the therapeutic suggestions that follow.

——————————————————————————■——————————————————————————

Category two imagery in general is suggested for older or more sophisticated children and early teenagers. Induction imagery should allow the younger client to explore the possibilities of using their own creative and imaginative mind to see what might happen. Older children may be resistive to the notion that they must do something and do not need an explanation as to what will happen in a state of deep relaxation. Oftentimes expectation of a positive experience may be enhanced by allowing them to enter into an experiment with the hypnotherapist and take part in determining the type of imagery that is the most relaxing and meaningful to them.

No matter how sophisticated a teenager acts, the hypnotherapist should be aware that there is a youngster inside the teenager as well as the adult. This youngster may be termed 'The imaginative, creative you' for therapeutic work. Therapeutic results may also be enhanced by allowing the teenager to understand that it is OK to daydream and create new and imaginative friends or solutions to problems like they did at a younger age. This kind of creative thinking and feeling is not a measurement of their physical and emotional maturity, rather it is a sign of their inner abilities to create future possibilities and unlimited rewards.

Floating in Outer Space

Now let yourself pretend that you are in a space capsule or a space station and you are going to experience a new feeling of floating in space. Close your eyes and pretend you are putting on a space suit that is keeping you comfortable and helping you to maneuver and float in space. Floating in space is a fun thing to do and it's easy to do if you are wearing the space suit. And the suit you are putting on is the perfect size and color for you. And you know it's the perfect suit for you as you relax deeper and deeper asleep and put your arms into the jacket. Notice how light your arms are as you put them into the jacket. Pretend you are putting on the jacket and your whole body feels light and relaxed and the jacket feels good and it is just right for you. You may see yourself putting the jacket on or just now that you have put it on and as you close the front of the jacket you feel more relaxed. So very relaxed now that you are picturing and imagining putting on the space pants and your legs are so light and relaxed and when the pants are on your whole body feels so light and relaxed.

Let that feeling of light relaxation happen now, make it happen and enjoy the feeling of going even deeper relaxed and your whole body feels good the more relaxed you are.

I am going to count from five down to one and with each number you are feeling deeper relaxed and slowly beginning to float in your special suit and the more you relax the better your suit is and you can picture and pretend to be floating and feeling really good and you are putting on a helmet with your name on it and listening to the earphones in the helmet and learning and enjoying new things. And when you have the helmet on and are listening nod your head please. Very well, listening now to good feeling thoughts and words and things that make you feel good. And you can feel good like this anytime you want to by putting on your floating space suit and pretending to listen to the headset inside the helmet of your suit. And this is what you are listening to. You are sitting in this room and feeling good and feeling relaxed and pretending and this is OK because it a fun thing to do and a good way to learn new things. And you are listening to my voice and that's OK because your eyes are closed and you are feeling good floating in your special space suit.

Note: Therapeutic suggestions can now be given for the desired outcome of the therapy session. When alerting the young client you may wish to suggest that they will become more awake as they take off the helmet, pants and jacket of the space suit and prepare to return to the room they are in realizing that they can float in space anytime they want to by simply closing their eyes and pretending to put the space suit back on.

————————————————————■————————————————————

The Secret Place

And closing your eyes now and you can pretend to draw a secret place with a magic pencil and only you can see what you are drawing. You may be drawing a map to your secret place or writing down things that you want in your secret place or even drawing things in this place that make it fun to be in and only you can see the secret place. And you are pretending to go there and feeling relaxed and the more relaxed you are the more you can take to your secret place.

Now pretend that you are putting things to take to your secret place in a bag or suitcase or just wrapping them up to carry with you. As I count from five down to one you are putting special things into each bag and as you do the bags become more easy to carry as you go deeper and deeper relaxed so that on the number one your whole body is so relaxed and floppy and feeling good that your head hardly moves when you are so relaxed. And five, the head is so relaxed, and four, the body begins to relax and three, your arms are so relaxed, and two, you are so relaxed your eyes just want to flutter a little and stay closed and one you are picking up all the things you want to take to your secret place and are so very relaxed.

And you can pretend, see, hear and enjoy your secret place as long as your eyes are closed. And your eyes are so heavy now that the more you try to open them, they feel even heavier and you are enjoying discovering new things and seeing new things and finding new things in your secret place. And these are things that make you feel good and help you do whatever you want to do in school, in sports or learn about people, places and hidden talents and abilities you can use in anything you do.

And you know you are in your secret place because you can pretend to be or you know because you can see it with your eyes closed or you know your secret place just because you have made it the way you want it to be. And you are entering your secret place now and only you know what it looks like and where it is and when you are in your secret place nod your head please. Very well, you are learning new things now and feeling very good and relaxed in your secret place and listening and feeling even more relaxed.

Note: After alerting the youthful client, the therapist may wish to discuss some of the things the client took to their favorite place. This discussion should not focus on why they took a particular item or why they imagined this particular secret place because this is information that only the client should know. By noting items or feelings the client incorporated in their secret place, the therapist may wish to suggest some of these items as a part of induction imagery at the next session.

The Computer Game

Now close your eyes and pretend that you are a computer. Your head is the top of the computer and your fingers are the keyboard that can give the computer commands and make it work. Your eyes may want to move a little and that's OK because it takes a little time for the computer to warm up and become ready for work. And just pretend now that the computer is warming up and getting ready to play a computer game and the game is called turning off switches

And you are taking a big breath and feeling yourself relax as you begin to play the game. The way to turn off switches is easy and you are feeling more relaxed and turning off switches by simply moving the pointer finger on your right hand. And moving the pointer finger now and relaxing and feeling good and the computer is ready to play the game.

Each time you move your finger it turns off another switch and you are deeper relaxed and you can turn off switches and relax different parts of your body. As each part relaxes your finger becomes even more relaxed and barely moves as you turn off the next switch and relax another body part. And when a body part relaxes it feels good, like it is sleepy. The part may yawn or stretch or just feel different and you know that each part is resting like it was sleeping or pretending to feel tired and heavy and this is OK because you are in control of the computer switches and can turn them on or off as you want to. And moving the pointer finger and turning off the switch to your head and letting it feel relaxed and moving your finger and turning off the switch to your chest and your back and making it feel good. And your finger is so heavy it doesn't want to move and just the thought of the finger moving turns off another switch to the lower part of your body and your whole body feels good, the way you want it to be as you go deeper relaxed in this chair in this room and listening to my voice.

When the whole body is relaxed you are turning on a switch to the main computer and storing all the things you want to know and you know how to make your body relax and how to turn on the main control center for learning. And when the main control center is turned on you are moving your finger. You may not feel it move, but just think about it moving and turn on the center and when the center is on the finger moves again. Let the finger move one more time and you are ready to program the computer game.

And you can turn off switches and relax and feel good like you are relaxing and feeling now any time you want to do so by just closing your eyes and letting different parts of your body relax as you turn off switches.

———————————————■———————————————

Therapeutic Imagery for Children

Imagery for children can be developed by listening closely to what they want to happen in the immediate future. In cases where low self-esteem is an issue, the therapist can paint a word picture of the child being accepted or praised while pretending to do a task or interact in a situation where the child always wins. Emphasis is placed on a future activity or situation happening now the way the child would like it to be. For instance, "Pretend you are in school and the teacher is asking you a question and you know the answer and it is the right answer and the teacher is telling you what a good student you are."

Imagery for motivation can include a scenario of achieving goals for being good in an activity that the child is apprehensive about. Oftentimes the therapist can simply ask the child what would be happening if they were good at something. "Tell me what you would be doing if you were the best skier on the slope, what would you be wearing, where would you be skiing?" Another example might be, "If you had the best grades in your class, what would you say when the teacher called your name and said you had the best grade, how would you feel when other classmates asked you to help them get good grades?" By asking questions before a hypnotherapy session, a younger client will often tell the therapist what words or thoughts are the most inspirational and meaningful for them. Feeding back the young client's thoughts and expressions in a positive manner during hypnotherapy is an effective client-centered approach to hypnotherapy for children.

Visual and auditory memory can be enhanced in the same manner. The therapist may wish to suggest that the child is reading a particular book and their eyes are like the lens of a camera and everything they read is being recorded on film. When the child simply closes their eyes they are printing the film and looking at the pictures and remembering what they are reading just like they remember a picture that was taken of them when they look at it. Auditory memory can be enhanced with suggestions that the ears are like a microphone and everything that comes into the ears goes to a tape recorder or record that they can listen to any time they want to remember what they have heard.

Bed-wetting (nocturnal enuresis) and stuttering are childhood problems that may be associated with various psychological factors that deserve investigation before the use of hypnotherapeutic intervention and management. If these problems are not the result of a physical problem or deep seated emotional problem, the hypnotherapist can employ direct end result imagery for symptom removal.

Nocturnal enuresis may be helped with suggestions that the youngster see himself or herself sleeping on a dry bed and being aware of the feelings of having to go to the bathroom and letting those feelings alert them that it is time to wake up to go to the bathroom. Imagery that allows the child to imagine that the wet part of the bed is getting smaller each and every night can reinforce their progress.

Stuttering can be alleviated with imagery that allows them to formulate the whole thought or sentence and then speaking clearly and distinctly. While in a state of hypnosis the youngster can pretend to read a favorite story from a book and repeat the story out loud to the therapist.

Summary

Low self-esteem, self-worth and anxiety are contributing factors to problems faced by children that can be alleviated with hypnotherapy.

Establishing rapport with a child includes developing a friendship that allows the child to become actively involved in the therapeutic process.

A permissive approach to hypnotic induction and positive end result imagery is indicated for problems that can be ameliorated with hypnotherapy.

Child-centered inductions should allow the youthful client to exercise their imagination rather than dictate specific word pictures or expected results.

7

Hypnotherapy and Religion

Chaplain Paul G. Durbin, Ph.D., F. B. H. A

The question of hypnotherapy and religion often comes up during discussions of client-centered hypnotherapy. What are the important issues that may be of concern to a client who has a personal relationship with God? How can this relationship enhance the hypno-therapeutic process?. Paul G. Durbin, Ph.D., a United Methodist Minister, who is the Director of Pastoral Care at Pendleton Memorial Methodist Hospital and holds the rank of Brigadier General in the Louisiana National Guard, responds to these and other questions in this chapter.

One may ask, "Why does a person of religious faith need hypnosis?" I believe that question can be responded to by referring to a statement of Jesus in John 10:10 (KJV), "I am come that they may have life and that they might have it more abundantly." Hypnosis is one of the gifts of God which helps people experience the more abundant life.

Jesus said, "The spirit of the Lord is upon me, because He hath anointed me to preach the gospel to the poor, He hath sent me to heal the brokenhearted, to preach deliverance to the captives, and recovery of sight to the blind, to set at liberty them that are bruised." Luke 4:18 (KJV). Jesus called his followers to "preach the kingdom of God and to heal the sick." Luke 9:2 (KJV). These verses and others indicate that Jesus meant for his church to have a healing mission.

Obeying the commission of Jesus to heal the sick and in cooperation with a doctor, the pastor can use hypnosis to reduce pain, to lessen the side-effects of chemotherapy and to hasten the healing process. By properly using hypnosis, we can heal the brokenhearted, bring deliverance to those in captivity to pain, give sight to the emotionally and spiritually blind and set at liberty those who are bound by unwanted habits.

The first recorded use of hypnosis is found in the book of Genesis 2:21-22 (ASV), "So the Lord caused a deep sleep to fall upon man, and while he slept took one of his ribs and closed up its place with flesh; and the rib which God took from the man He made into a woman and brought her to the man." In this incident, God used hypnosis as an anaesthesia so that Adam felt no pain during the removal of his rib. Since that time, hypnosis has been used in almost every age and culture under a variety of names.

In addition to the references in Genesis, mention of hypnotic techniques are found in other ancient sources concerning the Egyptian "sleep temples." In the temples, Egyptian priests used hypnotic-like procedures to improve health. These temples were so popular that they spread to Greece and throughout Asia Minor.

Though he may have stretched his point, Chaplain W. Leo Peacock gives a number of New Testament illustrations of hypnosis. He makes a point with his interpretation of an account of Matthew regarding Joseph's dream about Mary, (Matt 1:20-5). He writes that this is a clear description of an individual being hypnotized and while under hypnosis being given a post-hypnotic suggestion on which he immediately acts as soon as he comes out of his hypnotic trance. The Scripture tells us that an angel came to Joseph in a dream and told him to take Mary as his wife. Upon waking, Joseph goes to Mary and they are married.

The practice of "laying on of hands," mentioned in the Bible, used techniques which are similar to hypnosis. In the 18th century, a Roman Catholic priest, Father Gassner, gained a reputation as a healer. Those desiring to be healed were brought into a room and told to wait. As their expectation mounted, Father Gassner would majestically enter the room, lower his cross on the head of a patient and command him to sleep. The person would collapse and upon command would rise praising God for the healing.

The modern history of hypnosis is considered to begin with Dr. Franz Anton Mesmer who was greatly influenced by Father Gassner. Over a half century ago, Dr. Emil Coué of France saw the power of suggestion. He taught people autosuggestion and his favorite phrase was, "Day by day, in every way, I am getting better and better." His methods were based on two principles: (1) "When willpower and imagination come into conflict, the power of imagination wins out, and (2) Imagination can be trained more rapidly than willpower."

One of the misconceptions about hypnosis is that it is anti-religious. Hypnosis is neither anti-religious nor pro-religious. it can be used for good or bad depending on the hypnotherapist and the subject.

Most religious groups accept the proper ethical use of hypnosis for helping people. Exceptions are Christian Science, Seventh-Day Adventists and some individuals of various denominations. In recent years, the Seventh-Day Adventists have lessened their resistance by using relaxation therapy and suggestion therapy. Though Christian Science practitioners and others opposed to hypnosis use the methods of hypnosis in their healing services, they denounce hypnosis.

In an address to the National Association of Clergy Hypnotherapists, Rev. Fred R. Krauss stated that religion has traditionally used hypnotic techniques in a variety of ways. The atmosphere of the religious service is geared to the induction of the trance state. The architecture, decor, and religious symbols have a profound spiritual effect on believers. The altar, cross, and flickering candles provide a fixation point for concentration and meditation. In prayer, most Christians bow their heads and close their eyes which can be a very similar experience to hypnosis.

Prayer hypnosis is a method I use when it would not be suitable to use a formal or traditional hypnotic induction technique.

I was asked to help a patient who was experiencing considerable pain but had religious reservations concerning hypnosis. I suggested that we pray together. I began the prayer, "As I pray, just let yourself relax because the more relaxed you are, the more effective this prayer will be. Now I want you to use your imagination so that the prayer will be even more effective. In Mark 11:24, Jesus seems to be saying that imagery with prayer causes the prayer to be more effective. 'Therefore I say unto you, what things soever you desire when ye pray, believe that ye receive them, and ye shall have them.'" Following this introduction, I used the imagery of Jesus coming and placing His hand on the area of discomfort. I concluded with the words of comfort and healing followed by, "In Jesus' name, Amen." Since this patient was very relaxed and comfortable at the end of our prayer, I suggested that she close her eyes again and drift into a peaceful and restful sleep.

Summary

A client with a close and personal relationship with God may want to investigate the Scriptures and discover that hypnotherapy is a healing gift of God and therapeutic results are directed by God if they choose this to be so.

The client-centered hypnotherapist can teach the religious client how to use the God given abilities they already possess to make a positive change in their lives.

Hypnosis is not anti-religious or pro-religious, it is simply a tool for enhanced physical, emotional and spiritual health.

Index of Imagery Scripts

About the Author

R.D. Longacre, Ph.D., F.B.H.A., has over thirty years of experience as an allied health professional, educator, clinician and hypnotherapy specialist in the area of visualization and guided imagery for pain management.

Upon completion of his medical studies at the University of California, Irvine, Medical Center as a Neonatal Respiratory Care Practitioner, he elected to pursue further training in the area of psychotherapy and hypnotherapy. He has completed internships in psychotherapy and hypnotherapy and has earned doctoral degrees in both Cognitive Sciences and Hypnotherapy.

Dr. Longacre is a Diplomate of the American Institute of Hypnotherapy and a Fellow of the National Board for Hypnotherapy and Hypnotic Anaesthesiology. He is a Past Chairman of the Council of Professional Hypnosis Organizations, Past President of the American Board of Hypnotherapy and a Past Member of the Board of Directors for several prestigious hypnotherapy associations including the National Society of Hypnotherapists.

Dr. Longacre is the Administrator of the National Board for Hypnotherapy and Hypnotic Anaesthesiology, a division of NBHA, Inc., and the President of the American Association of Catastrophic Illness Counselors.

Dr. Longacre's efforts on behalf of hypnotherapists has made it possible for members of the National Board for Hypnotherapy and Hypnotic Anaesthesiology to receive third party reimbursement for hypnotherapy services billed to insurance companies.

Dr. Longacre has received awards from almost every nationally recognized hypnotherapy organization and was inducted into the International Hypnosis Hall of Fame in 1991 for his outstanding contributions to hypnotherapy research and education.

Dr. Longacre resides in Arizona, where his private practice is limited to hypnotic anaesthesia and pain management in medical or surgical settings.

Other Books By
Dr. R.D. Longacre

Available From Kendall/Hunt Publishing Company

VISUALIZATION AND GUIDED IMAGERY FOR PAIN MANAGEMENT

A deluxe perfect bound volume that contains Dr. Longacre's classical techniques and clinical applications that were first presented in his book published in 1993, "The Principles and Clinical Applications of Hypnosis for Childbirth, Anaesthesia and Pain Management." The original book is no longer in print, however the concepts and How-To-Do-It chapters have been preserved in this new text written for professionals who specialize in Pain Management.

To order, call or write:
Kendall/Hunt Publishing Company
4050 Westmark Drive
P.O. Box 1840
Dubuque, Iowa 52004-1840
Phone: 1-800-228-0810
FAX: 1-800-772-9165